Lake Region Writers Network

Lake Region Review

Number 2 ● Fall 2012

Co-editors
Athena Kildegaard
Mark Vinz

Managing Editors
Anne Clark
Luke Anderson

Board/Staff/Readers

Luke Anderson
David Bengtson
Paul Carney
Yahya Frederickson
Reba Gilliand
Charlotte Helgeson
Ann Hermes
Athena Kildegaard
Chrissy Kolaya

Sonja Kosler
Heidi Kratzke
Linda Lein
Susan Montag
Lois Reff
Ann Schwalboski
Ruth Solie
Mark Vinz
Kevin Zepper

Production Editor
Joy Minion

Cover Design
Julie Brenden

Cover Art
"Cardinals"
Charles Beck

Lake Region Review

Lake Region Review is an annual literary magazine
published by Lake Region Writers Network,
P. O. Box 356, Battle Lake, MN 56515

ISBN 978-0-941127-51-6
© 2012 by *Lake Region Review*

Visit our website at **www.lakeregionwriters.net**,
find us on Facebook, and contact us
at **lakeregionwriters@gmail.com**.

Order copies of *Lake Region Review* by contacting us at the
mailing address or email address above, or through
the contact page at our website.

Printed in Fergus Falls, Minnesota

Contents

Introduction

It has been a hot, dry summer—a summer to test our mettle. But in air-conditioned comfort we've had the great pleasure to read some 430 submissions from writers around the region—writers who are undaunted by the whims of weather. Our aim in selecting writing for this issue is simply to look for the best writing that engages and enlightens through attention to language. In these pages you'll find characters challenged by circumstance (and weather), poems charged with vitality (and weather), and essays that will provoke and move you.

Many volunteers have made this volume possible: a group of talented first readers, keen-eyed copy-editors, a thorough database manager, and generous managing editors. Whatever the weather, all these volunteers are dedicated to nurturing and celebrating writing, particularly in this region of Minnesota. As with the first issue, it has been a labor of love.

Once again, our thanks to all who have helped so magnificently and to Otter Tail Power Company for its generous support. And thanks to you, dear reader, for without you none of this would be possible.

— Athena Kildegaard and Mark Vinz

Maxine Adams

Waiting for the Moon to Rise

The cemetery's tombstone teeth
stand silhouetted where hill and sky
paste themselves together.
Twilight sighs, we all come slowly sighing.

We are waiting for the moon to rise.

This place spins mist and memories of
long hair, dead dresses and stone-cut names.
The wind working to whisper them away.
All the while,

We are waiting for the moon to rise.

The graceless forms of twitching grass
and tangled Rose of Sharon.
Waltzing through the tombstones,
tripping feet and bumping shoulders.
Passing time,

We are waiting for the moon to rise.

And slowly comes the white disk's hour,
opening the moon's old cold lamp eyes.
Looking down on this dead pasture, measuring
the time lain down, and counted round, and counted round.

Shuffling, shuffling.

We are all waiting for the moon to rise.

Polio

Ellen Thorstad's scrawny arm held the screen door open to welcome Mom and me into her farmhouse kitchen. Mom handed her two loaves of homemade bread wrapped in a red and white checkered table cloth. It was her signature gesture of friendship.

"How's Vernon doing?" Mom asked.

Ellen's cheeks lifted into a smile punctuated by tear-filled eyes, "He's been waiting for you two all morning."

It was 1948. Vernon and I were eleven years old. Our moms, both named Ellen, had been friends since country school days. Vernon had recently returned home after a long stay at the University Hospital in Minneapolis. His doctors had declared his polio virus was no longer infectious, so our moms decided Vernon and I could safely be together and maybe become friends.

Vernon sat in his wheelchair at the far side of the kitchen near the open door to his first floor bedroom, once the family living room before he came back home. His mom wanted him nearby throughout the day. His rumpled plaid flannel shirt and oversized jeans draped like undone laundry around his collapsed body. His brown eyes glistened beneath a dislodged crescent of inky-black hair. He could have been the March of Dimes poster boy. A shy smile deepened his dimples as it spread across his face. I shuffled and shifted and managed to return my own shy smile.

Glancing over his shoulder, I spotted the iron lung in his bedroom. Mom had explained that Vernon needed an iron lung to help him breathe because some of the autonomic muscles around his lungs had been weakened by polio. The stainless steel tank looked like a silver submarine with riveted seams, bolt-ringed portholes, and protruding pressure gauges.

Vernon's mom rolled his wheelchair across the room to the kitchen table, then ushered me to a chair facing him. We sat suspended in dreadful silence. Our eyes avoided direct contact as we glanced around the kitchen. Neither of us could utter a word.

Mom broke the silence, "I baked some bread for you, Vernon."

"Ca-can I have some na-now?" He stuttered.

His mom reached into the kitchen cupboard and offered, "I have some homemade strawberry jam."

Our shared shyness melted as we chomped on mom-made bread and jam.

Vernon gestured clumsily and asked me to wheel him into his bedroom where the stainless steel iron lung dominated. His mom followed to demonstrate how this big tank opened like a clam shell. The smell of urine was strong. "Vernon has to sleep in here," she explained, "His lungs are weak because he had the worst kind of polio, the bulbar strain."

"I have to sleep in there so I don't stop breathing at night."

He seemed so casual about the possibility of dying.

Vernon's true passion became obvious as he reached his skinny arm into a heap of raggedy cowboy comic books on a coffee table in the corner. He pulled out favorites and recited verbatim the adventures of Roy Rogers, Tom Mix, and The Lone Ranger as he jammed his pointer finger into one pictorial frame, then the next. His stutter nearly disappeared, "When I get stronger my mom is going to t-take me to see westerns at the new theater in Hoffman."

Throughout our seventh and eighth grade years, Mom occasionally drove me to his house. Each visit revealed the great differences in our growth and how we viewed our futures. I grew broad-shouldered and athletic. I rode bike to school, played 4-H softball, helped neighbors with field work, showed prize-winning market barrows, and dreamed of playing football in high school and maybe even college.

Vernon did not attend school. He was tutored by a teacher who came to his house. Stacks of 45 rpm records of country western music gradually replaced his heap of cowboy comic books. His mom often drove him to see westerns at the Hoffman Theatre. He was diligent about doing daily exercises to build body strength to compensate for the atrophied muscles in his arms and legs. He needed rest at frequent intervals throughout each day. His breathing gradually stabilized until he no longer needed the iron lung.

Vernon and I rarely saw one another as we progressed through the same high school grade levels toward graduation in 1955. Each time I saw him he was sure to remind me, "When we graduate, I am going to walk up there to get my diploma with the rest of you guys."

*   *   *

The first game of the1952 football season was about to take place and I waited in my homeroom desk to be released with the team for the first varsity football game of my life. I was anxious and eager all at once, going over passing routes and blocking assignments in my mind. Mr. Bruning, the high school principal, stepped into the study hall and beckoned me, only me, no other players. Something was wrong.

I followed him into the hall where Mom stood weeping. Between huge gasps she said, "I just came — from Dr. Cain's office. — Ruthie has polio. — We've been quarantined. — You'll have to leave school — right now."

Mr. Bruning placed his hand on my shoulder, "Take all of your textbooks and school stuff home with you."

I wanted to scream, "I have a football game to play!" The urge was snuffed by the weight of Mom's news. My seven-year-old sister could be facing a future like Vernon's.

Mom drove Ruth and me to pick up our brothers, Stanley and Phillip, who were playing in the September afternoon sunshine during recess in the District 41 schoolyard.

While Mom talked with the teacher, Stan and Phil gathered up all of their readers, workbooks, and school materials and said good-byes. When the car doors clunked shut, we all knew it would be a long time before we would play with friends again. There would be no recess, no football, church, 4-H, or even trips to town.

Ruthie lay retching on the front seat of the car as we drove the three miles home. All three brothers sat uncharacteristically silent and erect in the back seat as Mom drove into the farmyard. Dad came running out of the house, scooped Ruthie off the front seat and carried her to his rocking chair crying, "Rutie, Oh Rutie, Poor little Rutie." He wrapped his only daughter in a blanket and rocked as he had when she was a napping toddler. He muttered out loud, "Where did we go wrong to bring on polio?"

We knew how the news of our quarantine would spread between cheers at the football game, and like flash-fires through rural telephone party lines, from bar stool to bar stool on Saturday night, from pew to pew on Sunday morning and there would be a story in the *Hoffman Tribune* next week.

Newspapers and magazines carried article after article about the latest polio flare-ups, mounting victim counts, and panicked warnings about avoiding the dreaded infantile paralysis. Public places like theatres and swimming pools closed. Pictures of toddlers struggling with their leg braces and ominous images of iron lungs tugged at peoples' sympathies for donations to the March of Dimes, to help victims and to find a cure.

A record number of over 57,000 cases had been reported in the United States by October 1952. Parents found it impossible to distinguish between reliable information and unfounded rumor. Mom and Dad harped on their best do's and don'ts: "Wash hands real good before eating. Don't play in stale or swampy water. Eat right and get your sleep. Keep flies away from food. Don't let your body become run-down or chilled."

Ruthie recalls the trip to the Sister Kenny Institute. "I had wrenching nausea, even when nothing remained in my stomach. My head felt like it was about to explode. I wanted to pass out, even die, to get beyond the pain. When I thought I couldn't take it anymore, I spotted the Foshay Tower from the backseat of the car. It was the tallest building in Minneapolis, so I knew we were nearing the Sister Kinney Institute."

Strangers in hospital uniforms, wearing masks, made clinking and flushing sounds as they scurried from room to room. Cries of pain and home-sickness echoed in the endless mint-green tile hallways. Several iron lungs wheezed air in and out, in and out. Orderlies delivered stainless steel carts of steaming hot towels stacked like cordwood to the hospital wards, and returned with piles of limp, cold towels to be sterilized and rerolled all over again.

Trained in Sister Kenny's special massage techniques, staff stroked arms and legs, and tucked steaming hot packs around young limbs. Specified regimens were repeated several times daily, day after day. The overcrowded hospital was an ant colony of repetitive therapeutic routines.

Mom and Dad felt guilty leaving their daughter in the hospital, yet they had animals, crops, and boys to take care of on the farm. They had no idea how bad this was going to be. Crutches, wheelchairs, or maybe an iron lung loomed as possibilities.

The following week their worst fears were allayed when medical lab reports showed that Ruthie had the Leon strain of polio virus, which is the non-paralytic variety. The great weight of guilt was lifted; however, she would have to remain at the Institute for another month or two of rehabilitation.

I was fourteen, Stan twelve, and Philip ten while we were quarantined at home. Aside from light school work and some daily chores, we were free to ride bikes, trap gophers, and hunt pheasants as long as we stayed away from local rivers and sloughs.

It was like a vacation from school. We played in the pasture woods, helped dad with fall field work, and rode bikes to places we had never explored.

We stripped our bikes of fenders, carrier baskets, and handlebar accessories to execute newly learned riding tricks. We performed in escalating rounds of bravado and sibling one-upmanship. We rode with no hands, coasted down the driveway while standing on our seats, rode while sitting backward on the handlebars, did wheelies, and made jumps off planks propped against hay bales.

One Sunday afternoon we performed our own bike circus in the front yard and rode until we were exhausted. Dad awoke from his Sunday afternoon nap to find us wet with sweat, wearing T-shirts in the chilled fall air. He punched his fist in the air and shouted, "You guys know better than to get yourselves exhausted and chilled. Are you TRYING to catch polio? We have one kid in the hospital already. Now get your jackets on and help me with the chores."

Sure enough, several days later Stan complained of a stiff neck and nausea. Dr. Cain drew a spinal tap and confirmed he had contracted non-paralytic polio. The Sister Kenny Institute was filled, so he was to be treated at home.

Four days later I awoke with a severe headache and gut-wrenching vomiting. I too had the Leon strain of polio, where gray-matter in the brain and spinal column becomes infected but does not cause paralysis.

We endured the same excruciating headache and dry heaves as sister Ruthie. Slightest body movements, even blinking of the eyes, brought on pounding headaches.

Our feet tried to curl under while our hamstrings and calf muscles knotted into charley horses. A stout sheet of plywood under our mattress straightened our backs, while a vertical footboard kept toes pointed up and calf muscles stretched. Bed sores appeared on our elbows, heels, and hips by the third week of squirming on the hard bed surface.

Mom administered Sister Kenny's regimen of massaging and packing our limbs in warm, wet towels with uncomplaining dedication.

We celebrated Ruthie's return home in time for Christmas. Our quarantine did not end until the first week of March 1953. It had been six months. None of us needed crutches, braces, wheelchairs or, thank God, an iron lung. We often reminded one another, "It could have been much worse."

*   *   *

Vernon's picture was included in The Chippewa, our Class of '55 high school annual. He had not been involved in extra-curricular activities so the space beside his picture was blank. He had, however, requested the following quotation be placed above his senior photo: "Diligence leads to success."

The day of our 1955 graduation ceremony, Vernon's dad opened the heavy glass doors of the new school gymnasium and his mother pushed his wheelchair into place where all fifteen of us graduates were seated. A pair of forearm crutches lay across his lap for his long-awaited walk. His eager brown eyes still shone under the familiar fallen crescent of jet black hair as he waited for his name to be called.

"Vernon Thorstad," the superintendent finally announced.

He struggled to stand and align his crutches for the biggest walk of his life. The room went silent as he positioned himself into a three point stance. His hips appeared disjointed each time he swung his braced legs forward. He established a rhythm of awkward lopes and headed toward his goal. When his hand touched his diploma, the auditorium exploded in cheering applause. A strong male voice called out, "Way to go, Vernon!"

He returned to his wheelchair, exhausted and triumphant. He had been true to the quote above his senior class picture: "Diligence leads to success."

*   *   *

Nearly a year had passed since we graduated from Hoffman High. I had been so eager to graduate and move on—to live in The Cities, to go to Augsburg College, to play football, find a profession, and be somebody. I left my College dorm room and walked across the quadrangle in the spring sunshine to pick up my mail in the student center on the way to my new part-time job at Fairview Hospital. My life was happening. I felt like spring.

Reaching into my P.O. box I pulled out a note from Mom. Enclosed was a clipping from the *Hoffman Tribune*. It read: "Vernon Thorstad, 19, dies of complications from polio."

I found a quiet table in the student center and buried my face in my hands.

The River Flows

My father tells me there is a field where the Otter Tail River flows into Otter Tail Lake, and each spring, as the winter snow melts, the field comes alive with wild crocuses in bloom. They flower in waves of purple, splashed with white and yellow, brilliant against the snow, as brilliant as a young boy's dreams. And as a boy he thought there couldn't be anything more beautiful. He sits in an old recliner that has taken on the contours of his bent shape. The Old Man talks with his eyes closed and sees the place. For a moment the eyes open, perhaps to see if that field lies before him. The blue of youth has drained from them, leaving a tired gray, and he sees that he is in his chair inside the familiar walls that have been his nest for many years. Through the fading eyes he perceives only vague shapes and varied shades. He closes them again, and in his faint smile it seems that for this moment he is free of the worn body, and he is a strong and limber boy, dashing across the ditch in his canvas shoes, breaking through the crust of the receding snow, and off into the field. He sees the crocuses even more vividly than he did then, their brilliance is indescribable.

The Old Man works his eyebrows, deep in thought, fighting to capture another image. The memories can be slippery, but he always grasps them in the end. He is sharp and as logical as always; it is his short-term memory, his leg strength, and his eyes that are failing him.

His white hair is thin on top; his complexion has softened from the coarse and windy leather of a younger old man to the red fleshiness of the sedentary. He is ready; the words come in a smooth flow, spoken in precisely the same order as all the other times he told the tale. He will pause at the same points, and the inflection of his voice will give weight and color at the right moments to best convey the scene as he recalls that near Bizerte, in Tunisia, they bivouacked in an olive grove. The Major, he smiles, told them not to destroy the olive trees, that the grove might be five hundred years old. They didn't. He bets he could go over there today and find that olive grove. There were burned-out tanks everywhere—some ours, some theirs. On one tank, HEAVEN, HELL, OR HOME BY CHRISTMAS was painted. Another read BERLIN OR BUST, over which somebody had painted BUSTED. The 82nd Airborne camped next to them. They put up night patrol, like us, he states seriously, but they ran double time. They were in better shape than us, I guess. An Arab stabbed one of their guards one night, so they put on a double guard.

It's time for me to go. I stand near his chair and wish him a good evening. He asks about my wife, and the kids. With each reply I take a step closer to the door. He says such nice things about my wife, and asks about work, the house, the kids' sports. I watch the clock on the wall, the one he made from a slab of plum tree he had taken from the back yard. My answers get shorter as I inch away. I doubt that he can see me, but I'm sure he can judge in my voice that I am leaving. Then he tells me I better get going. From the car I see him through the window, sitting in his chair with his head propped in his hand, and I move at an idle down the dark street.

It is a beautiful morning, I tell him. The world outside, beyond his vision, is draped in a heavy frost. The sun glitters on lacy ice that has crystallized on trees, rooftops, power lines. In the kitchen I rummage through the refrigerator, looking for something we can share. It's loaded with a bounty of leftovers from previous meals my sisters had prepared. I go with meatloaf and green beans. He'll like that.

"We used to call that hoar breath—some people called it hoar frost," he calls from his recliner. "That's hoar, with an 'h'."

I can envision his playful smile. I've heard this one before—we all have; in a household conservative in manner and language, little quips like this tickled the edges of our code of conduct and showed that we could have a little wicked fun without jumping with both feet into the pit of impropriety.

We talk and laugh as the winter sun quietly strips the ice from the world outside the windows.

The air is thick and muggy, and the evening sun is dampered by a smooth haze, but it's cool in the house. The air conditioner switches on and off regularly as I talk to my father. I warm up some left-over lasagna for him and help myself to a couple cookies. We settle in and he begins: They crossed the Atlas Mountains on a French-built narrow-gauge railway. The men crowded in cars that read: "40 Homme, 8 Cheval."

"That's forty men or eight horses," he smiles.

"The train moved so slowly up the steep grades that sometimes they'd jump off, throw their rifles over their shoulders, and walk. Their gear was held in the cars by cargo netting. Sometimes Arab kids would run out from the woods and slash open the bags and grab what they could—a handful of clothes maybe, and run off. We were given the command to shoot on sight, but we usually didn't," he said.

A pause in the conversation stretches into a prolonged silence, and he is very still in his chair. I wonder if he has dozed off, but then he shifts and I find he has been going over images of days long past. He remembers Deer Creek— this must have been in the late '20s, he supposes, before the Great Depression. One summer he and some other kids decided to dam up the creek to make a swimming hole. They played there every day—it was off the road, past a bend hidden by some willow trees.

"Usually we just skinny-dipped," he smiles. "The water would get muddy after you swam in it for a while, but it sure felt good on those hot summer days. I think word got out to some of the women in town that we were skinny-dipping, he chuckles, because one day we got there and the dam was torn down and the creek was just a trickle again."

Through the east window I see the arching spread of the old sugar maple across the street near the pond. Long ago, after a spring ice storm, Dad told me to pluck an icicle that had formed on a lower branch and taste it. It was sweet—nature's popsicles, he said. To be strong yet humble, a man of worldly secrets and earthy wisdoms, were things a boy should aspire to be, I was sure. A boy could be proud of a father like that.

"There were forty men to a barracks in the CCC's."
My father adjusts himself in his chair, and opens his eyes
to locate my shape. "We had to keep a fire burning in
barrel stoves all winter," he continues. "They were simple
wood buildings, no insulation—one group of guys just cut
firewood all day, every day—that was their job. It was an
FDR program to put men to work, during the Depression.
We got paid $25 a month, and you had to send $20 home."
He chuckles.

We fall into a silence and I piece together an image of
this man as he was at, say, my age. He is a man of peace who
has fought in a war. He has known the suffering of empty
pockets, but always ensured that we had enough. In his
daily manner he taught us to value honesty—justice—above
self interest. But my father is a pragmatic man. I recall how
he once told me, when it was clear that I was of age and
inclined to visit a drinking establishment now and again, that
if I got in a fix in a bar I should hold a beer bottle by the
neck and smash out the bottom on the bar. Then I should
thrust and twist the broken end toward my attacker.

In demonstration, he twisted his face into a terrible
sneer and growled, "Listen here, buddy…." He smiled at the
end of the act and looked for my reaction.

I threw my hands back like a guy avoiding a fight, and
laughed, "Whoa friend! I don't want any trouble."

One of the granddaughters lived with him for a while
when she was taking classes at a nearby college. They had
conversations deep into the night, and they grew very
close. He revealed to her things in his heart that we rarely
glimpsed. The strong man, the joker, had questions. When

he looked forward, to the end, he had questions. He had fears. They laughed, and sometimes they disagreed. Sometimes they prayed.

She saw him sit at the table in the evenings, long after we left. Sometimes he'd sit there with his head in his hands, tears streaming down his face. She said he was lonely, and he felt useless. And he missed Grandma Lu.

As he talks about the latest family news I pick up a book from an end table and thumb through it: *Favorite Poems*. I stop at one called "Highlands" and begin to read aloud.

"Oh, Robbie Burns! The old bard from the Scottish hills," he smiles. He picks up the verse and recites several stanzas, hesitating only once or twice to recollect a word. He wipes his eyes and yawns, and chuckles, then falls silent for a while.

"There was a Scottish guy on our transport to North Africa," he says after a few moments. "He was a big guy—nice guy, except when he was drinking. That was one big boat, I tell you. It was an old cruise ship that had been converted to a troop carrier. The guys were broken into two shifts, you got twelve hours on deck and twelve hours below. Halfway across the Atlantic we switched shifts. We were a chemical company, but the bulk of the 82nd Airborne were on board. We were on "F" deck, below the water line. When you slept on the top deck most guys wore their helmets so you wouldn't get your head stepped on. Every day there was an abandon ship drill—it was something for the guys to do. We'd put on a life preserver—Mae Wests, we called them, and jump over the side. You always kept your helmet with you wherever you went. You'd jump with your helmet. One night I was sleeping on deck when I heard guys talking on bullhorns. They were talking to other ships. They couldn't use radios or lights because there were German subs in the water. It turned out our motors were down—we were dead in the water. The rest of the convoy went on but they left us with a couple of little sub chasers. That was kind of scary, we were like sitting ducks. They finally fixed the big old diesels and we made it to Casablanca."

"Those were hard days," he says. The window behind him is streaked with rain. Dark figures of leafless trees bend to a cold wind on a gray sky. Dad looks tired.

"We hopped the trains, looking for work," he continues. "The freight yards were full of men, hanging around, out of work. It seems everybody was out of work during the Depression. I finally found a job at a farm, shocking wheat. They paid us fifty cents a day, plus room and board."

"Can you believe it?" he shakes his head and laughs. "Fifty cents! You couldn't get people to do that for fifty dollars a day these days. It was hard work, we worked right up to dark."

He lays his head into the recliner and closes his eyes.

"Then you'd get up the next morning and do it again."

"At the camp over the Bay of Bizerte they dug slit trenches in case of air raids. Often in the morning a single German plane would fly high over the camp to the bay, to photograph the watercraft gathering in the harbor for the planned invasion of Sicily. We called him Photo Joe," my father smiles. "They say that at one point there were four thousand craft in that harbor, from destroyers to LCI. They'd send up rounds at Photo Joe, but he always flew high, out of range. Whenever Photo Joe flew over, there was sure to be fireworks that night. After dark you could hear the German planes rumbling overhead, and then the anti-aircraft fire would start up and light the sky. Sometimes two land-based spotlights would catch a plane, and they usually brought that one down. All our unit had was a fifty caliber machine gun, with tracers every third or fourth round. One night a bomb fell in camp and we scrambled for the trenches. The first thing you do when you set up camp is dig trenches. That's why. The bomb was huge, but it didn't explode. It sat there, stuck in the dirt." He looks at me seriously, "We were pretty lucky, I guess."

I know this story and I marvel that the bomb did not go off. It was fated that he was to be a faithful husband and father of ten.

I was in a meeting in a conference room near my office, and I noticed that my office line lit up several times on the phone on the wall. I continued with the discussion, but I was distracted by the phone lights; there seemed to be urgency in the flashes. After the meeting I hurried to my office and retrieved several messages. The last one was from a sister. In a thin voice she said that Dad had a stroke.

He remembers a little cabin at the east end of East Leaf Lake. The lake bottom was littered with small flat rock. There were more weeds on that end of the lake, but the fishing was good. For walleyes it was a minnow on a bare hook with a heavy weight—no casting, just dropped over the side of the boat. Cane poles worked as good as anything. Grandpa fished for bass. He used a red and white Bass-O-Reno—that's what everybody used in those days.

He is in the ICU. The curtain to his room is open, and I see him in the bed from a distance as I approach. The Old Man looks small and worn. He doesn't see me enter the room, but he recognizes my voice and turns his head toward me. He greets me with a slurred chuckle. His face is pale and blotchy, and his snowy hair is thin and wild. The left side of his face droops slightly. He wants to know about my day and how I am, and did we have any luck fishing last weekend.

Between the red rims of his eyelids I catch a glimpse of his eyes. The irises are light, light blue; the color is continuing to drain.

The blood has pooled at the base of his brain, but it looks as though the bleeding had stopped—at least for now, the doctor cautions. It was now a waiting game, he says.

While the war was raging across the oceans, folks at home could keep up on the action through the newsreels that were shown in the theaters. One showed Italian forces invading Ethiopia, tanks and all, and the Ethiopians were fighting with spears. Haile Selassie was their king and hero as he directed the resistance.

The newspapers showed photos of General Patton with a pistol in each hand, firing at German planes. Eisenhower almost kicked him out of the Army after he had visited a hospital and slapped an un-scuffed but shell-shocked young soldier.

"'I don't want any goddam cowards in my outfit,' the General said."

"Old Blood and Guts, they called him—somebody else's blood, somebody else's guts." Dad becomes silent.

The doctor says he has fluid in his lungs, and the antibiotics should have begun clearing them by now. They are about out of ideas. The Old Man looks small and uncomfortable with the big oxygen mask. He tells us that he will go through two more nights with the bulky, chafing equipment, but if he doesn't get any better he wants the oxygen mask removed, and to be put on comfort care. He is so relieved, he says, so relieved that the decision has been made.

He tries to talk to us, but the rushing in the mask blows away his voice and his strength. Frustration clouds his eyes; a word exchanged with one of his children is much more important than breath. Sometimes he moves the mask aside and breathes out soft, pained sounds—words. A granddaughter bends near and he whispers into her ear. He calls us by his pet names. I try to talk to him but he cannot hear me and I don't want to raise my voice. He says the mask is like torture.

When Mom had collapsed on the floor, Dad performed CPR for ten minutes while waiting for the paramedics. They said the Old Man saved her life. After that he cared for her like a precious jewel, but he talked only of how she had served everybody so tirelessly all her life. He said that a lot of people these days find the idea of service demeaning, but she loved it. She raised ten kids and was liked by everyone she met. And you'll never find a harder worker than that woman, he said firmly. Serving others was what she felt she was born to do.

We are all there, at his bedside. The nurse explains what is about to happen, and then removes the oxygen mask. We take turns at the position by his head and hold his strong, warm and soft hands. We whisper in his ear and he nods through roughening gasps, and then we rotate to the back of the room in a blur of tears so that others can move up to his side. As we pass each other we embrace, tightly, more sincerely, more desperately than we previously knew how to. We recite the Twenty-third Psalm as best we can. He moves uncomfortably.

I wonder if he is afraid. I think that he is, and every time he shifts I think he wants to say, "Stop! Not yet!" Reverse the process. Not yet, not like this.

But at the same time, he wants to be brave. For us. For Lucille.

I think he is terrified and I want to bring him back, empty my lungs into him. I can't see a thing through the blur, but I feel the beat of the long and sweet song of his life. I think he has loved his life.

Now, a lifetime of belief put to the test. Is he ready? He has stopped shifting, and his breath becomes short and shallow. I notice his hands have cooled.

And then it changes. The spirit of the man has left the face. His skin is cool, gray, plastic. He is no longer with us. In the bed lies the worn, empty vessel, so small without the spirit. He has left.

He had whispered into a granddaughter's ear. Thank you, he had said. Soon I will be with Lucille.

The morning dawns slowly as the sun rises like a moonish orb through a thick fog. I slowly drive the silent streets eastward, and cross the river into Moorhead. At last the sun burns through and the vapor dissipates, revealing a landscape jeweled in dazzling white against a deep blue sky. The frost—hoar breath—is crusted thick and sharp on every limb of every tree, and hangs from the wires that run to the homes scattered in the countryside. The Old Man had worked in this river back in the 30's, down near Breckenridge, on a CCC crew clearing weeds and deadfalls.

I planned to swing south and find the interstate and home. On the map I note a string of towns with names that rustle distant memories, like recollections of the beloved toys of childhood: Ottertail, Parker's Prairie, Henning, Deer Creek. I keep bearing east. Ahead is a field alive with crocuses that bloom brilliantly against the snow, where the Otter Tail River flows into Otter Tail Lake. Beyond is an olive grove in Tunisia.

Frances Ann Crowley

If Life Imitated Art

The table, dressed in red damask,
would be aproned by a white table runner,
deep points crocheted at both ends.
The runner would have been on the linen shelf
anticipating this day, and would now
proudly display its deep, straight folds.
It would offer a tipsy basket of
grapes—red and green
and a loaf of warm, crusty bread on a stone.

There would be a bowl of thin-skinned apples,
some hazelnuts, an orange—partly peeled
'round and 'round—and a sharp knife
leaning casually against the plate,
and one pear—alone, aloof, bright green,
stem and leaves still attached.

I would arise on a sapphire-blue-sky morning
and waft down the spiral stairs in my
ever-so-slightly wrinkled, white-muslin gown and
drink the rich, dark coffee that would surely
be there, somewhere.

If you would join me,
so much the better.

Holly Dowds

Being Brave

Silent needles pass through cloth
quiet as a moth,
the pull of thread over and under
      allows the mind to wonder.

Yes, allows the mind to wonder
about generations past and future
while quilt-making for babies coming,
      but a nagging guilt; a brain-corner numbing.

Such but a nagging guilt; the brain-corner numbing;
some music could chase away that thought.
Tonight be brave and give that thought full rein:
      Oh god, it is the miserable ones.

God, oh god, it is the miserable ones:
the hungry and homeless and harmed,
seen in our cities and foreign nations;
      oh, the centuries of dominations and devastations.

Centuries, and more, of dominations and devastations
that I usually push from my cozy ruminations;
Usually closing my eyes to those terrible sights,
      wondering how they survive such a plight.

Wondering, wondering how they survive such a plight;
I recall the beauty carefully produced by
even civilizations at death's door.
     Anasazzi pots stained with geometric precision.

Not yet extinct, Anasazzi pots stained with geometric precision.
So many cultures famed for their artistry;
are these prayers to the gods?
     Or a way not to think of starvation, disease and war?

How not to think of starvation, disease and war?
which I barely understand,
     nor could endure;
          which I fear to examine,
               much less address.

I let my silent needles pass through cloth.

Black and White

Dad hunches forward in his glider rocker looking down at coffee stains and old burn holes that mar the once-blue seat cushion, signs of his life before coming to the rest home. I have my own scars, but I keep them hidden. I know that I cannot bring up my need for his affection now, that I've missed my chance. So we talk about the weather, what time is dinner, and then we talk about the weather again. When he yawns and rubs his eyes, my chest fills with relief like a child excused from the principal's office—I can finally leave.

I wait for a nurse's aide to unlock the door to the Alzheimer's unit and wish I knew the secret code like my sister Ann does. I see Dad waiting at the end of the hallway. When I wink and wave goodbye, he grins and gives me his special wave and slips back into his room. When the aide presses the magical numbers, the door buzzes and clangs like a jail cell, splitting my chest wide open. I'm free to go, but I feel ashamed at my eagerness to leave, so unlike the time when I was a young woman planning my escape.

Back then, Dad saw me, his oldest daughter, as the one who abandoned the family farm after graduation in search of Fool's Gold in the big city. Of all the family fledglings, I was the only one who got away. I ducked my last cow tail marinating in the gutter, working the morning and night shifts as a nursemaid to a barn full of Holsteins. I fled the hick town where I went to school between shifts, smelling like cow shit. A sorry bunch of stores lined up along a barren main street, with nothing in them anyone would want to buy. But then, if Dad had just once uttered those three little words, I might have changed my mind and stayed. But I was just 18-years-old. All my thoughts were in black and white.

I'm sitting very still in my car outside the nursing home remembering all this, and my heart sinks as I think of my sister Ann who had no choice but to stay.

When Dad became a widower three decades ago, Ann became his keeper—the daughter who would try to knit together the hole that raveled when Mom died. She was the eldest daughter at home when Mom left us. Only 15—a tender age to be fixing and patching broken hearts along with the never-ending yarn of chores that wrap around life on the farm. Her teenage years were patterned to fulfill Dad's dependence on her, not the independence most teenagers sought outside the home. If she joined friends after school, who would mend the rips and tears in the growing pile of farm jackets and overalls? Since then, Ann has evolved into our family's rock, but she will always be a diamond in Dad's eyes.

My mind shifts back to the first day I pulled into this parking lot, the day when my siblings and I moved Dad to the nursing home.

I arrived too late, maybe on purpose. Who wants to evict their father from his hard-working life and convince him it's time to lie down and die? More than one of us saw him driving on the wrong side of a four-lane highway, cruising through stop signs, and taking shortcuts across neighbors' lawns. Living alone was a new set of hazards:

forgotten lit burners, prescriptions neglected or taken too many times, slipping in the bathtub and the forever-burning cigarette left unattended on the table's edge as the ashtray was too full. As a family, we agreed that Dad could no longer live alone, but it was natural for Ann to make the transition as seamless as possible.

Ann cornered the home's administrator, insisting our father be served frequent, small meals to reduce his digestive distress. She double-checked his clothing, ensuring the labels were marked with his name to avoid getting lost in the wash. Dad, a heavy smoker, battled with kicking the habit, but Ann convinced the home to allow him an occasional pinch of snuff. She couldn't bear to take everything away from him.

During my visit today I saw the names and telephone numbers of his eight kids penciled in large print on tablet paper, hanging at eye-level on the wall by his phone. But his fingerprints were smudged under only one name. Dad always calls Ann if he needs something or wants to chat. She's always been there for him. Why would he call anyone else? Before I left, I highlighted my name and number with a yellow marker. Even though I was so anxious to cut our visits short, I still wanted him to call me, to let me know he was thinking about me, too.

Back home, days turned into weeks with no call from my father, so I picked up the phone and dialed his number.

"Hi Dad, I'm coming over for a visit. Is there anything you want me to bring?"

"Sugar lumps. They don't have any sugar lumps here."

Today, like every day, the nursing home ticks along slow and hot and quiet. I scan the dining room where the residents are playing bingo. Four white-haired ladies sit at a table, heads drooped, hands clutched in their laps. I wonder if they're sleeping, or maybe they're praying their numbers get called. Alvin, Dad's roommate, sits alone, his shaky fingers shuffling colored bottle caps beside his playing card. While I'm looking for my father, the aide walks up to me, points at Dad's room and says, "He's having a bad day."

I peek around his door, walk in and stop with a start. I'm startled by the changes in him since my last visit—rheumy eyes that are more distant, ruffled hair a lighter shade of gray, and a pale face etched with yet more weariness. He sees me staring and nods at me, his shifting eyes tell me he doesn't know who I am. But he smiles like a little kid when I hand him the box of sugar cubes.

The sugar producers no longer use the word lumps. Lumps have no shape. Cubes, like dice, have six perfect sides, symmetrical to conform to our artificial world, complex like a Rubik's Cube. Dad's mind conceals broken springs and screws like those used in the puzzle, his thoughts and actions don't line up just right. But he hasn't forgotten sugar lumps were like candy when he was young. He clamps a sugar lump between his dentures and slurps his coffee.

We flip through pages of farm magazines I've brought to fill up his empty days. He pauses to look at pictures of green John Deere tractors like the ones he used on our farm years ago. I flinch when he flings the magazine on the floor and turns to stare out the window, his fingers twitching, his breathing the closest he comes to conversation.

I try to envision what's going through his mind, when he asks, "Cindy, why do I need to stay here—here in the nursing home?"

I pull my chair closer, holding his hands and calmly explain, "Dad, you're not allowed to drive anymore, and we worried about you living alone. The staff here takes care of everything for you. You don't have to remember when to take your pills or make your own meals." Resting my hand on his shoulder, I chuckle, "And, hey, I know how much you hate to wash clothes."

His defeated face droops. He twiddles his thumbs. I wish I had the power to turn back the clock for him. Life is not fair. I feel like telling him, *I know you don't want to be here. Let's go somewhere else and you can do whatever you want.* But I don't.

The room feels hotter than it did a moment ago. I dab a tissue on my forehead as I remember sweat trickling down my back as I stacked hay bales on the Fourth of July back in 1965. Dad had promised a picnic and swimming at the lake after the hay was baled. The work done, we waited in a fever of excitement. Watching Dad calmly doing his daily chores, I realized we weren't going anywhere. My father had broken his promise.

Ann never breaks her promise to visit Dad every Sunday. She senses when he yearns to escape the clutches of the home. Ann signs him out, and they drive to her country home, taking the long way, so he can gaze at fields of oats and corn. Before taking him back to the home, she surprises Dad with his favorite meal—baked ham, mashed potatoes and boiled cabbage with lots of butter. Just like the old days.

But I remember the old days, and wonder if my mother was as happy as she pretended to be. Whenever Dad worked in the fields, she never knew when he would get in, but she better have supper on the table. He had a habit of leaving a small heap of food on the edge of his plate. I never knew if he was full or wanted to leave a reminder that the food wasn't quite tasty enough. After smoking his after-dinner cigarette, he crushed the butt into his leftovers leaving an unsavory meal for the dog. As he pushed the plate away, I can still hear him taunt: *Very spectacular meal.*

I crush that memory and continue my vigil to pump him up. "The home has so many fun activities—listening to local musicians, going on bus rides out to the country, and, hey, you could be playing bingo right now."

His questioning eyes are now pleading. "I want to go back to the farm. I need to plant the crops."

Should I tell him he sold the family farm many years ago? I swallow my thoughts when our conversation makes a huge U-turn.

Staring at the wall, he asks, "Who are those people?"

I stand next to his cork bulletin board with tattered photographs, each with numerous pinholes after he's tacked them up over and over again. Pointing at each picture, I re-acquaint him with these strangers: his wife, daughters, sons, grandchildren, great grandchildren; and one-by-one, put a name to the young faces of his mother and father, his brothers and sisters, who stand stoic in the 60-year-old black and white family portrait. For a moment, his eyes light up and then fade away into nothingness. After my futile attempt at a family reunion, Dad's face is a jumble of sadness and confusion. I feel I'm as much a stranger to him as the lifeless people on the wall.

I feel the pull of Mom's eyes staring at me from her high school graduation picture, surrounded by photos of grandchildren she never knew. She was 18 when she had accepted my father's hand in marriage, the same age when I fled from that same farm. I look deeper into her eyes and see my mother shortly before her death, leaning with weariness against the sink, her body gnarled and swollen, scars of a hard life. I swipe the tissue across my eyes, wishing I had spent less time searching for gold and more time with her before God took her hand. I don't see in black and white anymore.

I look at Dad with a new pair of eyes, and cradle my hands around his face. He covers my hands with his own and I lean over, wrapping Dad in my arms. His strong bear hug breaks my heart.

"I love you, Cindy."

"I love you too, Daddy," I say, pushing my crumpled-up face into his flannel shirt. My thoughts tumble back to when I was eighteen. I don't want to let go.

But Dad releases me and hooks his thumbs under his suspenders, puffing out his chest. "Let's have another cup of coffee."

Feeling my pulse slow down, I breathe differently, more deeply and reply, "Okay, just half a cup and then I'll have to go." We drink coffee together. He talks about the weather and what time is dinner, and then he talks about the weather again. But I'm only half listening. My mind keeps replaying the words I waited so long to hear.

Against all odds, today I found my way into Dad's heart, right next to Ann. I was given a second chance before it was too late, before the Alzheimer's stole my identity. For the first time in years, I'm going to rest easy. My conscience is on the mend, and it will heal more with each visit. I will tell Dad how anxious I was to yank free of my country roots when I was a teenager and head for the intriguing, bright city lights. I will tell him I discovered that, although the city was enchanting, it was also congested, polluted, nerve-racking and impersonal. I will tell him I saw strangers in cars, sitting next to each other at stop lights, looking straight out the windshield, never at each other, living parallel lives. I will tell him I came to my senses and raced home to be with him again. I will tell him I wish I'd come sooner. I will tell him how much I love him, again and again, so he doesn't forget.

I walk to the door with a spring in my step. Looking over my shoulder, I wink and raise my arm for our special wave, but Dad's eyes look down and sweep the floor, trying to find the words that are on the tip of his tongue.

I wait, expectantly, until he asks, "Ann, could you bring me a can of snuff next time you come?"

I pause for a moment and say, "Sure, I can do that."

We exchange waves and as I walk out the door, I hear him say, "See you next Sunday."

Yahya Frederickson

Carthage

Tunisia

I step down into the stark morning
at Hannibal Station. As the train
disappears toward Tunis, the children

who got off at the same stop
flock to the shop
of the man selling popsicles.

I do not know the way
to the ancient city from which
a battalion marched

until alpine flowers stained
the feet of elephants crimson.
I ask the man, wondering

in which language he will answer.
Up the hill, a colonnade
of stout palms summons no shade.

There, he might point, that way,
down the hill, and I will find
the stone paths where

Roman children etched games
another stark day millennia ago,
beyond the flats and railways

of today's children of Carthage,
who flurry past me, laughing
with tongues of orange ice.

Yahya Frederickson

Ruins

2005, Palmyra, Syria

The camel man has only two, so our twins pile onto a hump
while my wife and I duel
over who's not going to ride.
It could have been

the first camel ride in her entire Middle Eastern life,
but I always lose
this kind of stubborn fight.
The camel man

concurs that I should ride. So here I am,
atop his tasseled beast
swaying over the bleak crust.
Three meters ahead,

two meters down, the camel man holds the reins
as he walks beside my wife.
He begins summarizing time for her:
the ancient kingdom

of Tadmor, another called Palmyra. A few sentences more
and he's all the way
to today, his cinder-block house.
With her, he's chatty

as he plods me past the Temple of Baal. I'm convinced
he's pagan.
My ship of the desert might as well
be an ass, or perhaps

I am the ass, rheumatoid, munching happily on jasmine
while my master
loads a bullet into his pistol.
Wrong time,

wrong place. I should just bray, dismount, and dance
the *dabka* with my wife
down the Avenue of Victory,
where Queen Zenobia

marched her centurions after beating back Rome's advances.
The camel man scratches
his address on a paper scrap. He wants
my wife to meet his,

so we can all be the best of friends, because it's good
to know each other's life,
good to know I'm feeding the hand
that bites.

Susan Gilbert

Good Night Moon, Good Night Haroun

Tiny fingers
card for comfort
whorls of my untamed hair.

Catch on a tangle,
tug fiercely
until free.

Your breath slows
to a shallow wet ripple
across the shell of my ear.

Genny

Margaret Grace Houlihan glared at the offending shoes. "I thought we talked about this yesterday, Audrey. You and I and Clarice agreed that flip-flops are not appropriate for sixty-five year old women. We agreed the feet of older women, like us, have become flat and wrinkled and not attractive. I guess our discussion fell on deaf ears because here you show up again with those abominations on your feet."

Audrey slammed the car door. "What discussion, Margaret? You were the only one talking if I remember right."

Margaret floored the gas pedal and the old Pontiac shot forward. Audrey exhaled. How the woman avoided accidents was a mystery. "Right living" would have been Margaret's reply if Audrey had expressed her concerns.

Silence reigned in the car as it hurtled down the street and roared into Clarice's driveway. The back door of the little house opened, and Clarice tottered majestically down the steps on severely spiked heels. She sat primly on the back seat and swung her feet into the car. Margaret turned to look at the shoes.

Spiked heels had also been the topic of conversation yesterday. Clarice and Audrey exchanged conspiratorial looks and burst into laughter. Margaret harrumphed and jammed the car into reverse. "Oh, give it up, Maggie!" Audrey chuckled as she dug in her bag, bringing forth sensible black flats. "Don't you wish we could indulge in a pair of great shoes again? Remember all the fun we had shoe shopping?"

The rest of the trip to the Hollow Tree Flea Market was spent reminiscing about great shoe shopping trips. Hollow Tree Flea Market sat in a hollow that baked in the hot summer sun. Flip-flops were sported by most of the attendees, and our girls wandered up and down the lightly-graveled paths.

"Look at that! A new vendor." Audrey lit out across the path. Margaret wiped the sweat off her brow and followed a bit slower.

As Audrey scoured for bargains, Margaret picked up an old stereoscope. Margaret's grandmother had had one of these. Heavy cardboard with two pictures on it was inserted into a holder in front of a view-finder contraption. The view-finder would somehow focus the two pictures and the viewer would get a three-dimensional effect. Grandma's stereoscope pictures were of great monuments, national parks, and landscapes. A scarred wooden tray lay next to the stereoscope and held the cardboard pictures. Margaret flipped through them. At the end of the tray, a stained envelope caught her attention. Several cards nestled in the envelope. A faded pencil notation indicated the envelope contained "Genevieve." Genevieve was her grandmother's name. Could these have once belonged to her? Margaret had no idea what had happened to Grandma's stereoscope and its pictures after Grandma died forty years ago.

Margaret slipped one of the pictures from the envelope and inserted it in the card holder. Old cardboard mustiness with just a whiff of tobacco assaulted her nostrils. She held it to her eyes and was surprised to see a person. A person? Margaret had never seen opticon pictures of people.

Lowering the stereoscope, she quickly flipped through the remaining pictures in the envelope. Yes; all six of them were of the same person. And, oh, my! Not very nice pictures. She once again looked at the picture in the holder and gasped.

A woman wearing only a very sheer peignoir posed against a blue drape. The peignoir fell open from her shoulders. Her left arm was raised, and in her hand she held a mirror in which she gazed at herself. Were there such things as pornographic stereoscope pictures?

Margaret lowered the stereoscope and took a deep breath. She returned the picture to the envelope, snatched three landscapes, and the stereoscope itself. Would the owner examine the envelope before he sold it to her? She'd be embarrassed. He'd think she was buying porn.

He chuckled when she lay down her purchases. "Yep," he said. "You found my porn stash." Margaret averted her eyes by digging in her purse. The owner continued as he bagged her purchases, "And, yes, there were porn opticon pictures. A lot of them were in color as opposed to black and white. They were expensive but men loved them and were willing to pay a little more. That'll be eighty-six dollars." Margaret forced a smile and forked over the money. Thankful she didn't have to explain herself and gesturing to Audrey that she was going to the car, she wobbled away from the stand.

Back in the car, Margaret carefully viewed all six pictures from the envelope. The same model had posed for all six. She studied them the second time and then a third. One of pictures commanded Margaret's attention. It was a close-up of the model—face and breasts. She studied the face carefully and slowly returned the pictures to the envelope.

During the ride home, Clarice and Audrey scanned her pictures. Each of their grandparents had possessed a stereoscope. Neither of them had ever seen pictures of people, much less pornographic pictures, although Clarice remembered her grandfather pocketing an envelope when she and her cousins dug out the stereoscope and the pictures. "Bet they were like these." She chuckled. "I wonder what happened to the gal who posed. Wonder what her story was?"

Margaret took a deep breath. "She married a farmer from North Dakota, moved here, had five kids, and died in 1965." Clarice and Audrey stared at her. "She was my Grandma Genny."

Margaret's fingers were still shaky the next morning when she dialed the number for Aunt Catherine's room at Greenwood Assisted Living. Aunt Catherine was her father's sister but the only family member of that generation left. Maybe being only one generation removed from Grandma Genny, she would know more about her.

Aunt Catherine's whispery voice answered as though she didn't quite yet trust the device. "Aunt Catherine, this is Margaret." Several seconds passed as Catherine sifted through 98 years of faces.

"Yes, Margaret. How are you?"

"I'm fine. I thought I would drop in to see you this afternoon."

Catherine chuckled. "Well, I'll be here." She broke into

song. "Don't get around much anymore."

Aunt Catherine was having a good day. "Do you still have those boxes of pictures? Maybe we could go through them?"

"Yes, they're on the top shelf of my closet. Anything particular you're looking for, Margaret?" The old girl was pretty sharp.

"Yes, but I'll talk to you when I get there." Margaret dropped the idea she could get some information from Aunt Catherine without revealing what she was doing. Best to be up front she thought.

Aunt Catherine's six boxes of pictures presented a daunting task, but they had been labeled by date. Margaret fetched the oldest box. "Okay, Margaret, what're we looking for?"

"I want to know more about Grandma Genny. Where did she live before she came here? How did she wind up in North Dakota?"

"Genny came from Chicago. She was different from my other aunts. All I remember is Dad's warning to not ask Aunt Genny too many questions. I once asked her if she liked it here. She said, 'This is where your grandpa lives so this is where I live.'"

"How was she different from the other aunts?"

"Well, she kinda held herself back. Didn't kick in with jokes and chuckles, but she smiled a lot. And she dressed different, with more style. Even though she was a farmer's wife like the rest of my aunts, she didn't dress like one. Ma always thought she was kind of uppity."

"Do you know what Grandma did in Chicago?"

"I remember something about modeling. It was never really talked about. In those days, models were of a suspect nature—down there next to prostitutes."

"Did Grandpa Harold ever say anything about it?"

"Your Grandpa worshipped the ground Genny walked on. He would never have said anything that would cast a bad light on her."

"How'd they meet?"

"My dad said Harold and Gunnar Eide had gone to Chicago to look at some cattle. I don't know where in Chicago they met, but your Grandpa went back a few weeks later. He stayed a week, and Genny came back with him. They'd gotten married at a courthouse there."

At the bottom of the box, a large Bible lay among the pictures. "Take it," Catherine said. "You're the only one who's interested in the family history."

An hour later, loaded with the Bible and pictures, Margaret barreled home. She spread the pictures of Grandma Genny found among Aunt Catherine's beside the stereopticon pictures. Using a magnifying glass, Margaret studied the face. Assuring herself it was the same woman, Margaret turned to the Bible. In the front on the page labeled marriages, she found Harold Johnson married Genny Mozinski on June 23, 1920, in Chicago.

— 1920 —

Gunner Eide and Harold Johnson stood in front of the stone arch entrance to the massive Union Stockyards on Chicago's Southside. Their tour was set for 1:00 and would last an hour. The clock on the center of the arch said 12:45. Gunner coughed. "The smell," he said. Harold nodded.

The smell had assaulted them since yesterday when they arrived at the hotel a few blocks from the stockyard. "Guess we hadn't planned on the smell," said Gunner. Harold again nodded in agreement. The two young men had traveled to the Union Stockyards in Chicago to witness the slaughterhouse operation. Ambitious and hard-working, they planned on building an operation in North Dakota. "Neighbors ain't going to like it," said Gunner.

"Nope, neither is Ma. We got enough land but it isn't nearly far enough away from the farmstead. If Ma were here, she'd put a kibosh on the whole idea right now."

"Well, let's take the tour and see what it's all about,"

An hour later, the two young men stood in the same spot.

"Sorry, Harold. Didn't think I was one to lose my cookies like that," said Gunner.

"Don't worry, Gunner. I thought I was gonna do the same thing."

Gunner said, "If the poor things hadn't looked so much like the ones we're raisin'... Don't know if I can send them away now that I know what's going to happen to them."

"As long as I don't have to see it, I reckon I'll be alright. But I don't know as I'd be able to have an operation like this on my land."

"Ah, you'd get used to it." The voice came from behind them. Turning, they saw Genny Mozinski for the first time. Slim, with a camel coat wrapped around her and a brown cloche pulled low over her forehead, she was leaning against the arch. One knee was bent and her foot rested on the arch behind her. The men, speechless and awestruck, stared as she exhaled from her cigarette. "My brother works here." Her voice was low and sultry. When the men didn't reply, she continued, "Smells bad all the time—the stockyards—and him."

Harold cleared his throat and removed his hat. "I'm Harold Johnson and this is Gunnar Eide. We're from North Dakota."

Thus began a whirlwind, three-day tour of the city conducted by Genny Mozinski. In later years, when Gunnar remarked that those days were three of the best days of his life, Harold replied, "Every day spent with Genny is the best day of my life."

In the week following the trip and back in North Dakota, the boys were asked about the best thing they saw in the "Windy City" or "den of iniquity." Gunnar named the sculpture of the fighting bull elephants outside the Field Museum or the Ferris wheel on Navy Pier. Harold always replied, "Genny Mozinski." No one in Granville, North Dakota, was surprised when, after a week, Harold returned to Chicago. Neither was anyone surprised when, after another week, he returned with a wife named Genny.

— 2012 —

Margaret noticed Gunnar Eide in many of the photos she got from Aunt Catherine. She randomly picked one and looked at Gunnar looking at Genny. The date declared the picture was taken in 1931. Harold looked at the camera; Genny looked at him, and Gunnar, on the right, looked at Genny. The next picture showed the three of them sitting on a downed tree. The back of the picture noted it was taken after a tornado in Ayr, North Dakota. Again, Gunnar looked at Genny. "Hmm...," thought Margaret. "Gunnar looks as though he had more than a passing interest in Genny." She rifled through the pictures and the Bible. A loose corner of the paper covering the back of the Bible captured her attention. She examined the paper. Glue tightly held the outer edges of the page on the back cover, but the middle of the page was loose and thicker. Margaret dug out her steamer and carefully loosened the paper. With one side loose, she fished out two thin notes. One, on filmy blue paper, was dated August 13, 1931.

August 13, 1931

My Dearest Genny,

I have no right to call you that. You are the wife of my best friend. I would do nothing to hurt Harold, but in my heart you are my dearest. I have kept silent about my feelings for these many years and can no longer. Tears have flooded my face many times after having spent the evening with you and Harold and have had to go home alone. You have been in my bed, in my dreams. We have sat together in church, in my dreams. We have raised children, in my dreams. For many years, my dreams have sustained me. They do no longer. I must tell you how I feel or, at some time or some place, I will inappropriately reveal my feelings. I cannot risk destroying my friendship with Harold if that should happen. The three of us have spent a lot of time together. I am afraid that must be curtailed. You and Harold and your lovely children must have Sunday dinners without me, not all the time, as that would look suspicious. When Harold needs extra help, please do not join us in the shop or barn. Let us not sit together in church. When we do

*not run into each other in our normal haunts, tell Harold I
am seeing someone. At some point, I hope that will be true.*

*And I must tell you this—my love for you is not
the only secret I have carried. In 1923 when I returned to
Chicago, I visited a shop that would be embarrassing to
admit to. In that shop I found some stereopticon pictures of
you. You were, and are, lovely. I bought the pictures, tracked
down the photographer and learned the story behind them.
He, after some physical persuasion, assured me the ones I
possessed are the only copies. I have put them away and will
never refer to them again and will never share them with
anyone. I will be honest and tell you that I have looked at
them several times. As I said, you are lovely. My dearest
Genny, anytime you need me, I stand ready to serve.*

Gunnar Eide

Margaret didn't realize she was holding her breath. She
inhaled deeply. The other note was in an envelope which
read "*Upon my death, return to Genny Johnson. If she has passed,
please burn. Please do not read.*" It was signed Gunnar Eide.
Feeling guilty, Margaret removed the letter.

August 26, 1931

Dear Gunnar,

*Thank you for your note. I wish I could say I knew
how to react to it. It has taken several days for me to
compose this in my head. You are such a dear friend to both
Harold and me. I cry when I think of our (your, mine, and
Harold's) relationship not continuing, but you are right.
Curtailment is a must, but not discontinuing. Harold*

*would miss you too much, as would I. I must say, I have
felt your devotion and have puzzled over it. I pray that the
"someone" you talk about will become a reality. She will
get a loving husband, and you will delight your children by
being a great father. The picture issue needs to be addressed,
I suppose. I am not proud of that part of my life, but
the taking of them kept my only brother safe. Jonathon's
gambling had spiraled out of control. Creditors (that is
too nice a word for them) approached me about doing the
pictures to release him from his debt. I did. Enough said
about that. Thank you for taking care of that dark side.
Much love to you and know you will always have a special
corner in my heart.*

Your dearest Genny

Margaret reached for a Kleenex and blew her nose. She
folded the papers and gently slid them back into the Bible.

The following Sunday, Margaret returned to the Hollow
Tree Flea Market—this time alone. A booth sporting flip-
flops stopped her. A red pair with glittering straps captured
her attention. They were cute. She slipped off her sensible
sandals. The feet were still wrinkled but they didn't look
bad. Some red polish on the toenails might be fun. Margaret
figured by the end of the day she would be used to the peg
between the toes.

The vendor was there. She approached without any
trepidation. "Do you remember me? A week ago I bought a
stereopticon and, what you called, your porn stash."

"Sure. I remember you. Slightly embarrassed you were."

"Yes, I suppose I was. Do you remember where you
got the pictures?"

"Yep. Found them in the trunk of a 1931 Chevy that my grandpa had parked in an old shed."

"Who was your grandfather?"

"Eide," he replied. "Gunnar Eide."

Thin Ice
In Four Pieces

I may have been born blind. Legally that is. I don't know. My earliest memory contains only smell and taste and effort: a baby crawling onto our battered oak table, straddling a large can of pineapple juice, and then lifting the punctured holes to my mouth, to taste the shocking sweetness.

While other toddlers imagined shapes in the clouds, I held to my eyes rocks veined with stories from the Ice Age. Even though I was tall, my first grade teacher sat me in the front and allowed me to scoot the desk up to the blackboard. By now my parents must have known I could not make out the large E at the top of the chart. Still, with books pressed up to my nose, I learned to read.

When my older sister Eva was ten, she took all the money she'd saved from helping our grandmother, who took in laundry, and rode the train ninety miles to Rapid City. She walked toward downtown and then asked a woman on the street, "Where is a place to buy glasses?" With no help from our parents, she bought a pair. Then she took the train back to Philip. But I was not as resourceful or as brave as my sister and there was no longer a train between Philip and Rapid City that carried passengers. Like Eva, I received my first pair of glasses when I was ten, but our parents drove me to the optometrist and paid for them.

They arrived in the mail and I found the package on our round oak table. My brothers charged into the house behind me. School lunchtime provided twenty minutes to walk home, twenty minutes to walk back, and ten minutes to eat, so my brothers pushed directly to the kitchen where they jockeyed and fought to find and fix something to eat. I ripped open the package and slipped on the cat-eye frames. Everything snapped into hard, sharp edges. I looked at the door out to the east porch. It was covered with nicks. I looked up and saw the pocks in the acoustic ceiling tiles. As I lowered my eyes, the front windows swept to the side. When I peered in the mirror by the telephone, there were two me's: a clear, narrow face inside the brown frames of the glasses and a bigger fuzzy one outside the lenses. Which one was the real me? My eyes hopped between the two. I felt dizzy.

"They don't look too bad." Buba trooped by with some sort of sandwich.

A pot had clanged and I now smelled Campbell's tomato soup. Hanky whined that Bud should let him have some.

Bud wandered into the living room tipping a soup bowl into his mouth. He sat the dirty dish on the table and banged out the door without noticing my glasses.

My little brother ran after him and hurled a spoon at Bud for not sharing the soup. It thunked against the outside door and clattered on the porch floor. In the kitchen, I sliced a wide chunk of my mom's bread, spread it with commodity butter, and threw it butter side down into the fifty-gallon drum of sugar under the counter. Outside, the world was an intoxicating whirl of leaves and swaying daggers of weeds. I tried to eat the butter and sugar sandwich on my way to school, but the earth sprang before me like a rabbit and my steps landed flat-footed and jarring. I shuffled forward like walking on thin ice. I felt nauseous, but we never missed school and we were never late. I threw the sweetness onto an ant heap where it wouldn't go to waste.

*   *   *

Bud inspired me. He was two years older, old enough to look up to, but close enough to be close. Bud could take a washing machine apart and reassemble it, but he did not do well at school, which meant he was given the shit chores. One of those jobs was milking our cow Red.

Fetching Red from the nether reaches of the pasture was part of the job. Bud, creative soul that he was, decided to reduce the workload by riding Red to the barn. He simply looped a rope around Red's neck and climbed on her back, and Red, who knew Bud intimately and had a full udder aching for relief, tolerated it.

When Red strolled to the barn, Bud sat atop her like a prince, bobbing and swaying and smiling at the rest of us kids like he had the best job in the world. To make the vision complete, he needed only tinkling bells on his ankles. I watched as an envious eleven year old for a whole summer. Then I'd had enough.

One hot bored afternoon, I took the rope from the barn and headed out to the pasture to find our cow. My tough bare feet picked their way slowly to avoid cactus. My heart drummed with excitement. I'd never ridden anything except my grandma's Saint Bernard when I was about five. But, riding Red looked easy enough.

I found the cow not too far away, down in the draw

by the dried up dam where green still grew. She looked up, curious, and then continued to graze. I approached and patted her shoulder.

"It's okay, Red."

She looked up again, eyes rolled toward me, suspicious. What the hell was going on? It wasn't milk time. I wasn't her milkman. And no one casually sauntered out in the pasture to chat with her. She didn't lower her head.

I patted her again and she switched me with her tail.

"Shhhhh, that's a good girl." As I slid the rope around her neck, her body tensed. I belly flopped onto her back, heaved my leg over and barely had time to grip the rope before Red took off running.

I pulled back on my makeshift reins, which had no effect whatsoever. I wasn't Bud and I didn't belong on her back. She twitched with me bouncing and gulping and gripping that rope. The ride was thrilling and terrifying. Then Red headed for the barbed wire fence. If she couldn't throw me off, she was going to scrape me off.

I let go of the rope and rolled away from the fence, but on my way to the ground two barbs caught near my ankle, one cutting light and long, the other ripping short and deep.

Lowing in alarm, Red trotted off toward the barn, the rope dragging behind her until it finally slid off into the withered buffalo grass. The fall hadn't hurt much, but blood streamed to my crusty heel. I hobbled toward the house and wiped the bottom of my foot on the back porch mat. When I entered the kitchen, I walked on the ball of my right foot, but I still left a dripping path to the bathroom. I sat on the edge of the tub, turned on the cold water, and let it gush over the gouge in my leg.

My mother followed the blood trail and found me there. "What happened to you?"

"I got bucked off the cow and my leg caught on the barbed wire."

"Let me see."

I turned off the water and the ankle looked momentarily better.

My mother grabbed my leg and twisted it toward her. She frowned at the two-inch hole, which started to pour fresh blood. She rummaged through the stack of mismatched face cloths on the open shelves, and handed me a pink one almost worn through in the center. I pressed it against the cut.

"What put that fool notion in your head?"

I don't know what to say about that moment. I don't remember it. My brother Bud does.

Unlike my brothers, I'd never been much of a liar. And I was talking to Mama, so maybe I thought it was safe. It was a bad cut that needed stitches, so maybe I was just thinking about my own leg.

"I saw Bud do it."

My mom left the room.

The cut wasn't life threatening so I never went to the hospital.

Bud, on the other hand, did go behind the outhouse. My dad never hit his baby girl, but that didn't mean someone wouldn't pay for this bloody mess.

Bud silently served as a whipping boy, defending me, his little sister, with his back. During my youth, my wide pink scar reminded me only of my big adventure. It took my brother to remember for me my betrayal, but he never held it against me, never even told me until I was an adult. He carried that shard of my life, my duplicity and blindness, and didn't return the piece until I was grown and ready to be complete.

The occasion was our first family reunion. A bunch of us were sitting on the steps outside our childhood home, waving away flies and drinking ice-cold Budweiser from sweating cans, as we swapped "poor stories." As Bud regaled us with the riding Red saga, he slipped in the beating as simply another detail.

"You were beaten?" I sat shocked, the beer suddenly burbly and sour in my hollow stomach.

Bud rolled his eyes. He knocked on the top of his stomach to make himself intentionally burp.

In that glaring South Dakota sunshine I realized that everyone I had ever encountered might carry a sliver of my identity like that: as sharp and sparkling, as hard and ephemeral, as a splinter of ice. And, I needed every fragment to be whole, to have a true picture of myself.

I wondered what it had cost Bud to carry my blindness all those years. I fished for some shiny secret sliver to offer in return, to reflect his identity for him—my amazing, inspirational brother.

But Bud only laughed, with a wisp of bitterness, at my surprised face. Then, the best storyteller among us, he moved on to getting lost in Disneyland.

*   *   *

Here I reflect Bud's tale.

At the end of fourth grade, I was farmed out to take care of my three little nieces in Wyoming, and my mom was off to college at Spearfish. My dad, not quite sure what to do with all the boys left at home, loaded up Hans, Bud, Buba and Parker, ages eight, twelve, thirteen, and sixteen, and in two days drove them to California to visit their oldest brother Wayne. But Wayne had a job and his wife worked, too. They were okay with my dad spending his days at their house, watching television, napping and reading magazines, but my four brothers were another matter.

So, the next day Wayne crammed them into his Volkswagen bug and dumped them at Disneyland. He bought each of them the cheapest packet of tickets. "If anything happens, if you get separated, you meet right here, and you be here at 5:20. Don't get in trouble."

They trooped around getting the lay of the land—all brick road and green grass and castles. They felt like they were inside a movie.

"It's like an exploded miniature golf course," Bud said.

The four of them huddled and calculated how many tickets they had and what was possible.

"Let's start at the arcade," Parker said. "It's cheapest."

In the arcade, they spread out to investigate the games. "Come here!"

They congregated around Bud and a red upright machine. It didn't look like much. Two metal grips stuck toward them. "It tests how much electricity you can take. Watch this." Bud slipped in coins and grabbed the bars. Their eyes fixed on the meter that shot up until Bud couldn't take it any more. The readout let them all know that Bud was tough, but not close to a champion.

"What's it like?" Hans asked.

"Like an electric fence, but it doesn't zap you, it starts real gentle. Who wants to go next?"

"I have an idea," Parker said. "I'll grab one handle and Buba can grab the other and we'll all hold hands with Hanky and Bud in the middle."

It was a good way for all of them to play for cheap and with the electricity passing through four bodies, they ran the needle up to the champion level.

They strutted away, plucking their tee shirts from their chests, bumping into each other and others, shouting out names for themselves: The Electric Crusaders! Super Electricity! Super Conductors! The Franklins! The Franklinsteins!

They came to a fountain where a lump of dry ice caused the shallow water to bubble merrily.

Without discussion, Parker reached in, grabbed the ice and ran. His brothers sprinted after him. The ice burned like licking a playground pole in January on a bet. He bobbled it into a basket of his tee shirt, which caused him to run one-armed and awkward. He stopped on a small arched bridge where visitors leaned on a rail to view alligators. The dry ice burned even through his shirt. Parker hove the chunk into the lagoon and everyone watched dumbfounded as the water roiled.

A bearded tourist looked at them and then looked at a security officer on the far side of the bridge.

The four boys took off running. The officer was no match for their long skinny legs, but they pumped, anyway, splintering around clusters of people, and at one long line of Japanese students, Bud went left while the other three dodged to the right, and when Bud reached the end of the uniforms, he found himself alone. He saw a gate to his side and climbed into a secluded area, a place where he could stop and try to spot his brothers.

Strangers threaded by on the paths. He didn't panic. At age nine, he'd been separated from his Cub Scout troop in the Badlands, but spouted on the front page of *The Pioneer Review*, "I wasn't afraid because I had my scout knife." At age ten he had set the front weed patch on fire with a bottle rocket, but had beaten out the flames with his pants by the time the fire engine arrived. And when he was eleven he had floated down Bad River stranded on an iceberg.

He turned to see what was behind him and spotted an ordinary door, like it might be an office, so he opened it. There was Snow White, sitting stooped over, rubbing the arches of her feet under her slippers. Across the room the Seven Dwarfs were in an irregular line at the coffee pot with the tallest one in front distributing cups. Goofy's severed head sat on a table, while a man's head on top of Goofy's body smoked a cigarette. None of them were singing or dancing. None of them looked at him in a very friendly way.

"How did you get in here, kid?" Goofy had stood and latched on to his shirt.

Bud pointed at the door, but couldn't speak.

Goofy pushed him toward a security officer, a different one than at the bridge. The man grasped him by the shoulder, but not too roughly, and steered him to a small office. He sat Bud on a chair and seated himself at a desk.

"What's your name?"

"Bud. Nelsen."

"Are your parents in the park?"

Bud shook his head.

"It's customary then to have an officer drive you home. Where do you live?"

"South Dakota."

The officer huffed, exasperated, and looked at him. "Pierre?"

He pronounced it like a French man's name and Bud wondered if the whole outside world pronounced the state's capital that way.

"Peer," Bud mumbled.

"Is that how you folks say it?" He folded his meaty arms and Bud stared at the golden hairs.

Then the man lit a cigarette.

"You have anyone in the park with you?"

Bud nodded, but didn't rat out his brothers.

After another minute or so, the officer led him back out to Disneyland. "Do you know how to find them?"

Bud nodded again. He followed the map in his pocket back to the entrance. He stopped and stared at the open arches where only air marked the division between the world of asphalt and cars and whining and the world of winding paths and bright rides and joyful canned *It's a Small World*. It struck Bud how a person could step over a line and move from one reality to another, just like electricity jumping hand to hand, or dry ice moving directly from solid to gas. The thinness of the separation terrified him like no security guard ever would.

He stood frozen for a moment. Then his brothers swarmed up to him and sang, "Bud got caauuught!"

He wondered why they thought he had been caught and not just lost, but caught was vastly superior so he said, "I need something to drink."

They were all thirsty from running, but at the concession stand they stared at the shocking red plastic numbers. They dug around in their pockets and counted their change.

"Let's go together and buy a quart," Parker said.

"I want Coke," Hanky said.

"Yeah, Coke," Buba agreed.

"7-Up," Parker said, and because he was oldest, they bought 7-Up.

As Parker twisted the cap off the drink they jumped on a trolley, each in his own seat, to rattle back toward the heart of the park. Parker gulped the drink before Hans pounded on his back. "Gimme some!"

He spilled 7-Up pulling the bottle away from Parker. He drank, burped proudly, and passed the container to Bud whose mouth was paste from the encounter with the officer. Bud guzzled the liquid until Buba hit his shoulder. He passed the bottle back.

"There's nothing left but spit!" Buba shoved it back at him.

Bud tipped the bottle and drank to the last drop. It might have been spit, but after you'd been yanked from one world to another by a decapitated Goofy, it tasted like 7-Up.

*   *   *

One conversation can change a life.

Ever since my Uncle Cecile and Aunt Dee died, I believed the same story. One drunken night, Uncle Cecile had chased Aunt Dee with a hammer. She had run out on the ice to escape. The ice cracked and Dee plunged into freezing water and drowned. Cecile died from exertion trying to pull her out.

My Uncle Cecile had met Aunt Dee when she worked as a maid at the Senechal Hotel in downtown Philip, South Dakota. Rumor said she offered more than fresh pillowcases. They made a good match as wild drunks together, the type who got arrested for public intoxication and barroom brawls.

As a child I knew this and didn't care. Whenever my Uncle Cecile and Aunt Dee visited, they brought us kids salted peanuts and sometimes plastic bags of orange peanut-shaped marshmallow candies.

One afternoon, while my husband and I sipped margaritas on the deck, I told him about Uncle Cecile and Aunt Dee.

"Did anyone ever look to see if there were hammer marks on the ice?" my husband asked.

"Why would they do that?"

"Maybe he wasn't chasing her with the hammer. Maybe he got it to break the ice."

"Wow!" Cecile had been trying to save Dee, so maybe my husband's version could be true. Maybe he had not been trying to kill her with the hammer. I swirled my margarita as my long-held belief melted like the chipped ice. Maybe it was alcohol induced, but when my perspective shifted, the whole picture changed. My uncle grew more heroic. Hadn't he, during The Depression, run away from home at age fourteen to find work? Hadn't he been a sergeant during the war? Hadn't my father, a decorated veteran himself, looked up to him?

"Was there an investigation?" my husband inquired.

"I doubt it." Philip, South Dakota had fewer than one thousand people. Everyone knew my Uncle Cecile and Aunt Dee. The two had died in the middle of nowhere. People knew what had happened, and neither the town nor the county had a CSI unit.

I took another sip of margarita. "Wow."

But at the family reunion, I overhear my mom and sister Jazz discussing Cecile and Dee. It stirs me from ninety-degree-weather-induced torpor.

My mother and sister are sitting at the table, reminiscing.

Mama is recounting how once Daddy went to Rapid City to spring Aunt Dee from jail. He'd thrown her in the back seat of the car, and even though the woman swore like a sailor, all the way home she pleaded with him to pull over because she had "to take a tinkle." My mother, who has become a bent little old lady, all wrinkled skin sliding off bones, relishes the story, enjoys mimicking the babyish voice of my aunt.

"Tell about how they died," I prompt.

Cecile and Dee went to a country dance, got drunk, and were dropped off at their long unplowed driveway by another aunt and uncle. For some reason, maybe it was easier than post-holing through snowdrifts, they decided to walk home along the frozen creek. Even though she was just a twig of a woman, Dee fell through and Cecile died trying to save her.

"Didn't Cecile chase her with a hammer?"

My mother turns her kaleidoscope eyes on me. "Goodness gracious. A hammer? Where on earth would he have gotten a hammer? There's no hammer in the story, just thin ice."

My uncle shrinks back to size. Neither a hero nor a villain. The story flattens like a watered-down drink. And I think of the reliability of all the stories of my life. Do I remember crawling on the table as a baby, or do I imagine it because I've been told the story? In the end, it seems, I am an unreliable, nearly blind eyewitness to my own existence.

Audrey Kletscher Helbling

Taking Lunch to the Men in the Field

Three o'clock. Lunch time.
My brother grips the tarnished handle
of the rusty red Radio Flyer as the wagon bumps
along the dusty dirt drive, dipping and curving
past the cow yard mucked with mounds of manure,
toward the stubbled alfalfa where the men are making hay.

Our mother has stowed sandwiches—
slices of coarse, yeasty homemade bread slathered in butter
with rounds of spicy summer sausage slid in between—
inside the tin tub next to chewy oatmeal peanut butter bars
wrapped in waxed paper, nudging brown beer bottles
that jostle and clank as the wagon rolls.

She's packaged the lunch in a crisp white cotton dish cloth
embroidered with *Wednesday Wash Day*
and stitches of clothes clipped to a clothesline,
mimicking the laundry she's hung out earlier,
now stirring in the wisp of a July prairie breeze.

My brother and I lag under the heavy heat of the afternoon,
straining toward the men working the field.
Dad, shaded by an umbrella, guides the International along
    the windrows
while our bachelor uncle heaves hay bales onto the flat-bed
    trailer,
his chambray work shirt plastered against his back,

his grimy DEKALB cap ringed in sweat
as he toils in an unbroken rhythm of labor.

We reach the edge of the field as the men finish their round
and the racket of tractor and baler ceases
giving way to our small voices which break the sudden
    silence:
"Lunch time. We are here with the beer."

Nancy Klepetka

The Women Who Look Like Me,
My People

Legs strong, stumps of old oaks tethered into the earth
Thick abdomens, like pickled cow's tongue in a jar
These Bohemian bodies, formidable yet soft
No scarf tied under the chin like my ancestor's babushkas
But my stout hands, broad face and nose reveal their DNA.

Backs like steam engines, carrying loads, never stalling
Gray days, gray skirts, dirt under our finger nails
Hearty laughter, robust appetites
Oxen-like resolve to carry out the day's chores
Perseverance engraved into lines around brown eyes and
     round mouths

We heave a deep breath into our lungs and move the rocks
     that are the world
Spirits full, rich, unbreakable
Nothing fragile survives here
Work, children, potatoes and root vegetables
The soil moves under us and through us until we return to it.

Karla Klinger

Cold

It's twenty below.
From the bus I watch the earth rush toward me,
snow packed tracks leading home.

Houses, aliens in the cold,
perch rootless,
children's drawings of rectangles and squares.
Trees beard the hills, defend against the wind.
Birds huddle together, won't fly alone.

I wish I could sleep through winter
like this ancient earth,
wake rooted when the first bud pushes forth,
let melting snow thaw my bones.

Karla Klinger

Hiking up

Just beyond the wild fields of purple
are aspen, birch and spruce,
woodchips on the mountain path.
We wanted a hike before dusk,
a panorama of the hills
and Lake Superior.

The ground is wet.
I step in your tracks
for the stretch and skill of it.
On either side, the forest floor
moves with yellow clover;
we debate which berries are poison.

Half way up,
a wolf print, alone
in the flat grasses.
I stay close, try to merge
our shadows. When the path
branches, we choose one

that leads us in a circle.
Birches give way
to evergreens whose roots
are tall enough to rest on.
Come see the view!

Near the top, birds
are gathering.
Suddenly,
a rush of sky.
The wind sings
a fierce vibrato.

Satellite Dish Snow Bowl

My house, Oak Hollow, was a splash of red in a world of white.

The dove-colored sky had shattered into bits and floated down to cover the earth in blankets of tiny, cruel diamonds. Sky fragments glittered white over a formerly black roof. Stately columns joined my ruby palace to the twin pearls of tundra and sky.

The oaks were many-armed gods, drawn in black calligraphy on a white page. Against the black-and-white beauty, cold arrived with the vengence of a thousand spears. It stole breath and sensation. It met me, edges sharp, blades keen for one who had not known cold before.

The cold of negative twenty degrees Fahrenheit burned like fire. Exposed skin seared as if blistered. Eyes pricked and ached. Nostrils tightened and stretched with hardened mucous that pulled nose hairs and blocked airflow. Lungs stung as they struggled to inhale the shockingly pure air: icy, frigid and hard.

I breathed in glass.

My new life in Minnesota was outlined in cold, circumscribed by cold, defined by cold, and determined by cold. Cold was my rubicon, my crossroads, my final test. If I could cope with the Minnesota winter I knew I'd be able to live here. Permanently.

"Have you been here through a winter?" was the second thing all Minnesotans asked upon meeting me, after "Ooh, yah, New York City to New York Mills, eh? Didn't want to change the address too much then, didja?"

When I answered that I hadn't yet lived through a Minnesota winter, the locals shook their heads and turned away. I wasn't a neighbor until I had lived through the winter and stayed anyway.

For my part, I knew that if I could make it through the Minnesota winter, if I could cope with extreme cold, then I would have earned my residency. I could be confident in my ability to stay and share a life with my new husband, Chris.

The internet went down during a snowstorm before a brilliantly sunny stretch of weather with turquoise skies redolent of tropical seas though the outside temperatures were ten to twenty degrees below zero.

The winds were blowing in gusts. The sky was clear as glass, blue-bright as only cold could make it. Two feet of snow on the ground had hardened into rockscape. My boots left jeweled caves in the sparkling sediment, foot-sized indentations with igloo-solid walls.

The internet satellite dish was a bowl of snow.

On the first day of my life without internet, I drove twenty miles and back through a snowstorm to a meeting that had been cancelled over email. On the second day, I called friends to remind myself they still existed. The internet had been the arbiter of my social life, allowing me to contact the world I had left behind in New York City and keeping me current with my new friends in rural Minnesota, many of whom had disappeared behind snow-covered driveways.

A week into an internet fast, I went to dinner at Chris's parents house and clung to their internet-connected computer.

"One more minute!" I yelled when dinner was called.

Everyone was waiting at the table for me. Chris's twelve-year-old niece and fifteen-year-old nephew had been peeled from their video games and were sitting politely, napkins on laps. I scarfed down too-large bites over small talk and rushed back to the computer to find Chris checking sports scores. I wheedled like a kid. "I wasn't finished!"

In that moment it became clear to me that I needed to get back online. This meant that someone needed to clear the satellite dish of snow. In my mind, that someone was Chris.

"Will you please fix the internet?" I stood over Chris the next day, in front of the couch where he was lying by the fire. The heat of the fire made a warm pool on my back.

"Nope." He sipped Genmaicha tea out of a pottery cup. "I'm not going out there." He pulled a faux-fur blanket further up his chest. "It's way too cold out."

I wanted to stamp my foot. I wanted to curl up next to Chris on the couch. I wanted to scream.

I dug slippered toes into carpet. This was an opportunity. This was my chance to be resourceful like my country neighbors. This was a challenge to the part of me that needed to prove I could live in rural, west central Minnesota.

I turned toward the door and assessed the situation. The satellite dish was attached to the roof above the garage twenty feet up from the ground. There was snow. The wind was blowing.

I needed a ladder and a lot of warm clothes.

I brushed the snow off the first rung of the ladder and

lifted my heavy, snow-booted foot. I transferred my weight to the first rung slowly, testing the hold.

Foot met ladder. My shoe's sole met the tread on the step. My foot held. I inhaled. Cold outlined my lungs in pain.

I lifted my other foot to the second rung, slowly lifting my weight upward. The third rung. The fourth. I looked out on the white world of Oak Hollow from a new vantage point. Emptiness. Clean white under turquoise. Glorious.

I reached the top of the ladder and stretched my body up. My mittened fingers made jazz hands a good ten feet short of the snow-filled satellite dish.

I couldn't reach. I needed more length.

I was resourceful. I was a country person. I could figure this out. I went back inside, wriggled my feet out of my boots and shed my outermost layers. In the laundry room I collected supplies: a new telescoping cobweb duster that I had bought on a whim, a broom handle that had lost its broom, and duct tape. After duct-taping the telescoping duster to the broom handle, a 16-foot pole reached through the doors of three rooms, flexing and dancing in my hand. I wriggled my new tool in victory.

I threaded the extended pole through the door to the garage, muscles tightening against the cold. I pulled against the tool's weight to balance it upwards, and watched the far end bounce and draw circles and swirls in the air over the tops of our cars. I teased the near end through the inner door and closed myself out with the cold.

I leaned my jerry-rigged contraption against the ladder, and it quivered into stillness. I took in the world around me. Me outside in the Minnesota winter: puffy yellow coat, oversized blue hat and scarf against the peppermint confection of whitewashed verandas and red walls. I was climbing a ladder perched on snow with slippery, snowy boots on a windy subzero day holding a 16-foot-long javelin.

I was a long way from my Brooklyn apartment.

I laughed and took a breath. Then I crawled, hand over foot, up the ladder. From the top, the end of the sixteen-foot duster just reached the satellite dish. I stood on tiptoe, my right arm extended as far as it could go. One clump of snow fell away from the dish and into the small space between my coat collar and bare neck. My blood pumped cold through my neck.

I reached further. My javelin went halfway into the bowl, but the yellow duster fringe had bunched up into an icy club. I needed more length.

I couldn't stop now.

In the warmth of the house, icy pellets at my neck melted and dripped into my shirt collar. I duct-taped the broom to the other side of the broomless broom handle to make a 20-foot, two-sided, snow dusting machine: one side soft for delicate duties, the other bristled for stubborn snow.

This time I was grateful for the slap of cold. As the pain of guitar strings had dug callouses into my musical fingers, the pain of the cold would callous me to Minnesota's winter.

My boot slipped on the icy tread of the third step. I clutched the rails of the ladder, and stabilized. I could do this. At the top, I twirled my spear upwards in an arc. Broom met bowl. Grenades of snow dropped in explosions of sky dust. I inhaled diamonds.

My arms ached. My abdomen shook. My fingers were numb. The satellite dish was half-empty. I hoped it was enough.

Leaving the ladder in place and the 20-foot-long pole bent in a curve that arced from white driveway to white roof, I pranced back into the house.

"How'd it go?" Chris was clattering dishes in the kitchen.

"It worked! I think. Hey, could you come outside and check that I've removed enough snow?"

As I reached to unlace a boot, I heard footsteps scrambling up the stairs.

"What are you doing?" I yelled through the ceiling.

"Checking the internet to see if it works." Chris's voice came through the section of ceiling under my office.

Melted snow dripped to the floor underneath me. I pulled at my second boot, constricting laces grabbing sock at my ankle. I hopped on one socked foot until my boot let go with a pop, then I ran, dripping and half-barefoot, up the stairs.

The computer was loading the Gopher basketball scores from ESPN's website.

"All right!" I yelled. I tried to shove Chris out of my chair. He pushed me right back.

"I'm not done yet," he said.

Judy R. Korn

Autumn 2010

Autumn comes like an angry teenager,
flies down the stifling hallway,
slams the heavy door,
locks the golden catch.

Leaning into the cooling timber,
she lingers a moment,
then lunges for the latch
on the north wall window.

Judy R. Korn

Deep Winter

I wake to the low rumbling of a snowplow.
A shrieking blade scores the blackened ice,
trembles the darkened lights suspended
between holiday and hangover and roof line.

Unyielding drifts, engorged with raw wind and grave cold,
creep past my windowpanes,
replace the stolen sunlight with colorless hollow.

I hazard gaunt streets, inch an arthritic vehicle
into intersections thick with haze, exhaust visible.

Silent Chickadees wait.

Ryan Kutter

Help Wanted

Muse, to fill existing position
after last applicant (the bum)
quit two days into the work.
The fellow before that was better,
but so full of angst
I had to give him the boot.

Ideal candidate will have
the selflessness to discover what's true
and the ego to talk about it.

Office works closely
with the Manager of Ambiguities.
Hours include the ungodly ones.

Must recognize there are no words
for what we're going through,
but say something anyway
to tide us over.

Ryan Kutter

Transmission of Power

Cicadas hum the way
I want to live.
Imperative, overwhelming,
utterly unnoticeable.

Once I thought the buzz
was a gust of energy
in the electric lines;
an urgent rise and fade.

Now I look into high brush
for a spare black body
reverberating
with burnt intentions.

I bear myself into the gullet
of that thin, blind pitch.

Julie C. Larson

Winnowing

In the stripped field, hands shielding my eyes
from the sun circling my grandfather's head, I watch
as he towers above me—god of fire, god
of sky, god of wind—astride the black steam engine's
back; thick arm raised like a hammer he signals the men then
pushes a lever and the flywheel moves
slowly at first, around and around, it groans
as it turns the long belt that tethers the thresher:
that great silver dragon, its monstrous mouth
open, roaring,
as faster and faster
the flywheel spins
and thunders
across the shuddering earth;
and the men's forks fly
laying sheaf after sheaf
on its dark tongue,
and it swallows them whole
to be battered
and thrashed and
battered again,
till the wheat kernels, clinking like coins,
are borne upward and out
in rivers of gold, spilling
onto the sunlit bed of a truck;
while the chaff's broken bodies, blown
through the air in dusty chuffs,

are heaped into piles to be burned, or
at best, serve as bedding for cows—as if
the stalks had never been buried deep in the ground and
raised themselves up tall and strong, holding the sweet
heads of wheat in their hearts; lifting them high, then
letting them go, letting them go, letting them go—
and at noon the wives, pale dresses
swaying in the breeze, pick their way
through the stubbled field, straw baskets
looped over their arms; they come
bearing milk and meat and
moist warm bread.

Norwegian Love

When my parents married in 1962, they moved to the old farmhouse where my dad had grown up. Actually, he had never left home and, at age eighteen, wasn't fully grown either. My grandparents had upgraded to a used, Liberty single-wide trailer and relocated within walking distance of the home place. True love could be the only reason my mother began this new chapter of life in this antiquated house. Mom had been raised in town with social amenities, such as running water and an inside bath. This decrepit house lacked both. Its four walls and roof also provided shelter to spiders, mice, bats, and an occasional farm animal with momentary special needs. After lugging soiled cloth diapers into town to be washed week after week, they finally got running water inside.

I was born nine months to the day after my parents married. My brother followed a year and three days later and my sister the following year; three under the age of three. But it wasn't because we were a good Catholic family. We were Norwegian Lutheran. It was then my parents must have discovered birth control, or were too exhausted or angry to touch each other, as there is a six-year gap between us three older siblings and the two youngest girls.

The two-story farmhouse had two bedrooms upstairs; one for Mom and Dad and the other for us kids. The enclosed narrow stairway was steep, and the distance between steps caused us to climb them on all fours, like climbing the ladder propped against the oak tree we used to jump off and onto the swing. Once upstairs, falling asleep was never an easy task. The walls lacked insulation, and on a typical winter night each exhale of breath released a little puff of smoke into the frigid air. The only heat source was a wall furnace in the living room below. A hole had been cut in the floor of our bedroom to allow the heat to reach us. If heat really did rise, it was escaping elsewhere. The three of us huddled together in a metal-framed twin bed with a painted wiener dog on it, combining our blankets for added warmth and shared body heat.

In the summer it wasn't any easier to fall asleep. We were sent to bed before sunset and nightly complained of this injustice. There was no window covering to trick us into darkness, since none was needed so far from the road. The window would be open anyway, in hopes of a breeze, and if the wind wasn't blowing or, more often than not, if from the wrong direction, our sweaty skin would stick to our dingy sheets, adding to them another day's play.

The eighty acres Dad farmed never yielded enough to provide for his family so he also worked a rotating shift at Tube Co., a metal tubing manufacturer in town. It was there that he acquired his stub finger but, as children, we loved to hear him tell of how it had been bitten off while fighting a ferocious tiger in Africa. When he worked the night shift it was even more difficult than usual to fall asleep. Not seeing him for days on end added to our list of grievances. Crying only made us hotter and our bed a bath of sweat and tears. Eventually we gave in to sleep, having worn ourselves out and been calmed by the serenading night songs of crickets.

One of our favorite sounds was the rhythmic puttering of the John Deere tractor coming in from the field. The putt putt growing louder and faster the closer it got until Dad shifted gears as he turned into the driveway. If we'd been quick enough to meet him, he'd stop and lift us onto his lap. We'd take hold of the steering wheel and pretend to drive; our tightly gripped hands jerking right and then left, pulled by the wheel, and our bodies tossing from side to side with the back and forth tilting of the tractor as its tires dipped into one pothole after another. But whether we got to ride the tractor or not, we were most excited that Dad was home.

One sweltering afternoon Dad came in from the field early, his overexposed skin hard to distinguish from the black film of topsoil sticking to his sweat. Mom had a church-ladies meeting at the neighbor's and put him in charge of us kids. As she drove off in the Chevy, Dad hopped in the bathtub. We were relieved it wasn't Saturday when we all took turns in the tub sharing the same water, all except Dad who always got his own. Curiously, afterward we'd inspect with pride his accomplishment of transforming clean water into the resemblance of weak coffee.

Elicia, the older of the two youngest sisters, was a toddler just learning to walk. Clad in only a diaper because of the heat, she waddled back and forth between the kitchen and bathroom while Dad was in the tub. He splashed at her playfully as if chasing her out. The bathroom door was never locked; the latch at the top, higher than the reach of little arms, was of no use since the door was warped and wouldn't close. Elicia waddled in one last time and slipped in a puddle of water. The thud of her head hitting the floor resounded throughout the house and we all ran to see what had happened. That's when we saw Dad—bare-naked—running through the kitchen with Elicia, unconscious, in his arms. His eyes screamed panic and fear as he bolted out the front door, heading for the trailer hollering, "Maaaa! Maaaa!"

We stood frozen in the kitchen, wanting to chase after but didn't, for fear that when we caught up to him, we'd see him naked again. It wasn't long before he and Elicia returned home, both conscious. Dad was wearing a pair of Fruit of the Loom briefs that he must have borrowed from Grandpa, but no one dared ask.

Dad, Mom, and Elicia got to stay up all night–doctor's orders. Although feeling slighted, we didn't view this as another injustice. We lay quietly in bed, reflecting on the day, remembering the look on Dad's face and the emotion that had sent him running naked. Even though he had never said the words, we had somehow suspected we were loved. The events of that day gave us one more reason to believe we were right.

Linda Frances Lein

Meltwater

for Keith

Our two sons
sprout tall
like young oaks
in the spring

while
we
shrink

like winter snow
that melts
to feed their roots.

Celebration of Life

His daughter

Thirteen years ago her father urged her not to marry Andrew Milner. They were standing here in his garage "workshop" while he was sanding a bookcase or bird house or something else he'd built as a gift. She could tell what wood he used by its smell. Oak smelled like honey. Alder was kettle-cooked popcorn. Ebony smelled like smelly socks. Cypress had a swamp smell—gaseous, or like cut grass, or compost, musk, or something. Or like a wet bathing suit you left in your gym bag too long.

He'd come here after supper. Sometimes, after homework, she'd join him just to be around him, letting him know she was there. She remembers sitting on that stool, not saying a word while he worked. She'd wonder what he was thinking while sanding down some long piece of wood with those repetitive back-and-forth movements—intent on scratching away flaws, smoothing out bumps, making it perfect.

Once, when he was sorting nails and placing them into their little bins, he talked about wood, maybe the longest conversation they ever had. Maple, he'd said, was hard and sturdy, perfect for floors or building bowling alleys. Oak would last forever and was moisture-resistant—great for boats. Pine was easy to work with, kept its shape and had those intricate whorls, or knots, that made it beautiful to look at. But be careful, he added. Those knots were also signs of weakness.

Years later, when he warned her about Andrew, he pretty much said the same thing. "Not him, Josie. There's no substance to him. Don't be fooled by his looks."

Today, the day of his funeral, or the "celebration of life," as they're calling it now, she sees the film of sawdust and shavings covering the cement floor, except where it's still wild with footprints, showing the chaos of a failed rescue attempt—which came hours after he'd collapsed and her mother finally went looking for him. Paramedics rushed him to the hospital, where he was pronounced dead on arrival. A stroke, they'd said. He died instantly.

She looks over this place, probably for the last time. She notices the hand sander has fallen under his workbench. She stoops to pick it up, remembering how meticulous he was about his tools, how everything had its place, how he wanted things to be there when he wanted them. But she's startled to see someone standing in the doorway.

"Omigod," she says, dropping the sander. "You scared the crap out of me."

Helen Mortenson is still tall and imposing, but starting to look her age—late fifties, maybe sixty. She owns a house two doors down with a big backyard she'd transformed into a garden showcase. Her once-dyed red hair is growing out gray, which softens her features and emphasizes her eyes. Her body is rounder, thicker in the middle. Her clothes are subdued for a change—browns and beiges—no longer the blazing pinks and oranges and reds that hurt your eyes. But she still smokes. A cigarette dangles from her fingers, jiggling up and down as she talks, a sign of her nervousness.

"Sorry," Helen says. "Nothing ever scared you before.

Maybe that's what living in a big city does to you." She takes a drag, blows out smoke, flicks away ash. "So how is Seattle?"

"Wet," Josie says, putting the sander back in its place. "Very, very wet."

Josie turns her back and continues walking around the workshop, touching items her father touched, absorbing each one, memorizing their textures and shapes, hoping to etch some durable picture of him into her mind. No one ever questioned his need for this refuge, or his wanting to be alone. She blames her mother for his need to escape. She blames herself for not getting him to love her.

"Norm did love you," Helen blurts out, as if reading her mind. "You know that, don't you? You were always his little girl."

Josie walks toward Helen, feeling mean right now, jiggling keys inches from her face, letting her know it's time to leave. "That's none of your business."

"You're right. It's not. I just want you to know how sorry I am. That's why I came. He was a good man." Helen is fighting tears now. "He was broken, of course; we all are ... in some way. But he loved you all, you know ... as much as he...."

But Josie motions for her to hurry up and get out. Then she slams the door shut, locks it, and heads back to the house, knowing Helen is watching her go, hating this woman for loving her father; hating her father for how happy he was whenever Helen was around.

His wife

I enter the dining room with the plate of cookies and rolls Gladys Fleischer, our next door neighbor, dropped off earlier today—twittering with sympathy, tugging at her sweater, eager to get away. "Something to tide you over before you—you know—drive up to the lake," she'd said.

Josie and Matt, my daughter and son, sit across from each other at the table. Josie is leaning forward, elbows on the table, clutching her cup of green tea, coiled, ready to spring. Matt is sitting back, his legs stretched out under the table. One hand caresses his coffee cup, the other inches closer to his groin, a slight smile on his face, egging her on.

I place the goodies on the table and sit at the head. He grabs a bismark and bites down, surprised by the squirt of jelly landing on his white shirt, in no hurry to wipe it off. Josie's fingers dance over the cookies before settling on an oatmeal raisin, lifting it politely with her pinky raised.

Karianne, Matt's wife, has moved to the couch, saying no thanks and continues paging through my latest *People*, ignoring the table conversation, listening instead for voices in the attic. Their three kids are up there rummaging through a trunk filled with old toys and will eventually start fighting.

"You can't tell me this is the first time some melting iceberg will flood New York under an ocean of water," Matt tells his sister. "This planet is—what—a gazillion years old? And this is the first time that ever happened?"

"That's not the issue," Josie says. "The issue is this is the first time the melting has been caused by us. We don't know what will happen."

"I'm sure the earth has survived so-called global warming for eons and I'm sure it'll survive again." He winks at Karianne with an I've-got-her-now look. But she ignores him, continuing to page through *People* with a little more snap in her wrist.

I rise from my chair and start stacking plates and gathering up leftovers. "I think I'll go upstairs and rest awhile," I tell them, refusing to intervene in this lifelong war. "We have some time yet. Sunset isn't until 6:30, right?"

"Six thirty-seven," Josie tells me, our family timekeeper. "You go ahead, mother, I'll clean up here."

Part of Norman's hand-written instructions "When I Die," was, no wake, no viewing, no casket—all underlined twice. He wanted to be cremated and his ashes tossed into Willow Lake just as the sun was setting.

His request is a mystery to all of us. The only explanation I can think of is that summer he was on strike and the children were little. We'd spend our days at Willow Lake, a cold, spring-fed body of water that stopped your heart when you first stepped in. We'd load up our station wagon with peanut-butter sandwiches, potato salad and watermelon and my chocolate-chip cookies, a thermos of milk, a jug of Kool-aid, some blankets, towels and bathing suits, dry clothes, balls, books and teddy bears; and we'd stake our claim close to shore. Norman, weighted down with supplies (like a pack animal in bermuda shorts and flip flops) raced to the beach, yelling that the last one there couldn't go swimming for an hour. He'd intentionally lose, of course, eager to stretch out on the blanket and watch the pretty girls go by. I was too worried about money to enjoy those long, languorous afternoons in the sun, wondering how we'd pay the rent or feed our family, or if Norman would ever work again. But his memories must've been different, because he wants to be dumped forever into the chill of that distant gray lake. And I'm not sure why.

I crawl into the bed I've slept in since our wedding night, a gift from my Polish grandmother who'd had it since her own marriage, maybe even longer. She presented it to us in solemn tones, like a priest blessing pilgrims on their way to the Holy Land. Or maybe it was a warning. "This is sacred thing," she'd said. "Is for love. It make your marriage a good thing. Or maybe not. Is up to you."

My bed comes in six pieces and is made of cherry wood. Whenever I move, it creaks and cracks, like the old oak tree outside our window when the wind is howling at twenty-below; but it represents warmth to me, a place of safety and rest. One night, when I wanted to fight, Norman tried to calm me down by explaining that cherry wood is known for its beautiful markings, and I told him to shut up. It's not about the wood!

He moved into our son's bedroom when Matt left for college, and then took up woodworking; and then he found Helen. She's a widow, who lives across the alley—a friendly sort, who stops and talks to neighbors while walking her dog. I'd see her and Norman standing in the doorway of the garage, shooting the breeze, wondering what she said that made him so effusive all of a sudden. Eventually, she came without the dog. And their conversations went on for an hour or two, behind a locked, impregnable, steel-plated door.

Well, that's what it felt like, anyway.

The children are still squabbling downstairs and Karianne is murmuring to her three little ones upstairs in the attic. I am sandwiched between two generations, and—unlike my Polish grandmother, who thought she was wise—I have no great insights to impart to anyone. All I'd tell them (if they ever asked; and, of course, they never will) is, do the best you can, which is not very helpful; because that's what they'll do anyway.

I look out the window and see white clouds filling the sky. How will we see the sun setting on Willow Lake if it's hidden by clouds? Norman's request still makes no sense. He continues to confound and frustrate me even after death.

I once dreamed the ghost of his dead father was poisoning our air like some lethal gas. I woke up fighting for breath and couldn't go back to sleep. But, somehow, the dream helped me understand my husband's cold nature and his inability to give of himself, which I thought was cruel and intentional, but must've reflected some awful childhood. Norman's reticence was maddening, but I eventually realized he was doing the best he could.

Josie suffered the most, I think. She's drawn to ineffectual men, thinking they held the key to some intricate lock that'll loosen the floodgates of her wild, true nature. She settled on Andrew Milner, unfortunately, a beautiful man with puppy-dog eyes, who apologized for everything he did. He left her for a woman twice his age; and they moved to the Ozarks to be near her grandkids. My daughter blames me for her failed relationships, and maybe for everything else going wrong in her life.

Now my husband is dead and I'm lying here alone on our wedding bed, wondering why I don't feel sad. I watch the play of light on my ceiling and remember our first year together as husband and wife: how Norman liked sex in the morning, how he moaned when he came and then quickly got up to get ready for work. I'd stand on the front stoop in my nightgown, feeling wanton and womanly, waving good-bye to my young husband, wanting neighbors to know what we'd been up to.

"Mother, we need to get going."

Josie is knocking on my bedroom door and I look at the clock. It's five-thirty.

"Coming," I yell back. "Give me a few minutes."

I go to the closet and pull down a cardboard box from the shelf, which holds Norman's ashes and seems weightless.

I should feel something, but I don't. I kiss the box, anyway, needing to wish him well, or bon voyage, or to show there's no hard feelings—or maybe to let him know I'm sorry and did the best I could.

I look in the full-length mirror, fluff up my matted-down hair, flick away some dandruff, straighten my black dress and head downstairs to rejoin my family.

His son

"Is your mom mad that we didn't bring the kids?"

"Probably." Matthew says. "She's usually mad at something."

They are on the road to Willow Lake, with Matthew and Karianne in one car, Josephine and his mother in another. He's following his sister who's driving her new BMW, which irritates him because she's being a big shot and needs to remember where she came from. He makes good money as an electrician, but with four mouths to feed you can't afford a fancy new car every two years.

"And besides," he adds, after giving it some thought, "they'd be cranky and drive us nuts. They're fine. Mrs. Fleischer loves to babysit."

Willow Lake is thirty miles northwest of Aspen Grove, a small city getting smaller every year because of young people leaving and never coming back: like precious water seeping through a busted dam, is how one mayoral candidate described it. Josephine moved to Seattle, working as a systems analyst. Matthew co-owns an electrical services company in Chicago.

They're driving on a leaf-littered country road, past trees at their peak of color—luminous yellows, golds, reds and rusts that light up an otherwise drab landscape and steel-gray sky. He'll be glad when this is over.

"You okay?" Karianne asks.

Matthew is rarely prepared for his wife's questions, which often unnerve him. He married a woman who demands honesty, which makes him uncomfortable, yet grateful at the same time. He is proud of Karianne's forthright manner and finds himself standing taller whenever she's around.

"Hmm? Yeah. I guess." Then: "Maybe not." Then: "No. I don't know."

She doesn't respond; and he appreciates her silence so he can figure it out.

The truth is, his dad was a complicated man and Matthew barely knew him. They never had those father-son discussions his friends laughed about when they were done assessing girls and had to keep the conversation going. As if these geezers can tell us anything! He'd laugh with them, pretending he had the same problem, but wondering why he and his dad never talked and then blaming himself for putting up barriers that kept his dad away. Maybe that was the problem. Him.

"I don't think I had a dad," Matthew finally tells his wife, trying to answer her question, but probably not making sense. "There was this man living in our house who had problems; and we formed a life around him and his problems—to survive without causing more problems. Does that make sense? Maybe that's what it was."

She nods her head, seeming to understand, but continuing to look out the window at the fall colors.

They're heading west where light streams from rips in clouds that are turning pale pink. Willow Lake is less than ten minutes away.

"But I loved him."

Matthew chokes out a sob when he says this, which surprises and embarrasses him. He covers his mouth with the back of his hand, needing to stop the rush of emotion. Karianne leans over to comfort him and he grabs her hand, holding on for dear life. "We'll be home soon," he assures her. "Everything will be okay."

He parks in the large lot that's empty except for Josephine's Beemer. His dad's remains are in a box his mother carries in front of her, like a priest carrying the sacred host. She looks terrified. He offers to carry it for her, but she elbows him out of the way and heads for the lake with purposeful strides, expecting everyone to follow.

They reach the end of the dock, and he realizes how odd they must look: a man dressed like an undertaker, three women in black coats, hats and high heels. Strands of pinks and purples and mauves are now threaded across the sky where the sun is a smudge of light behind breaking clouds. Waves splash against the dock, lulling them into a silence that echoes across the cold dark water.

Matthew looks around, amazed at the size of this small lake. It seemed oceanic as a little kid. He can't remember how old he was. But he does remember the rush he felt whenever his mother announced: we're going to the lake today. The car couldn't go fast enough to get here. He remembers jumping from this dock, petrified at first, but jumping deeper every day, feeling less fearful each time. Was it this shallow back then? If so, he never jumped into more than three feet of water. Is that possible? It felt so dangerous at the time.

He remembers his dad standing in the water, urging him on, telling him it was safe: you can do it, come on, I'll catch you. Could that have happened? His dad? Having fun with his dad? He remembers racing him from the car to the beach, winning every time, knowing his dad let him win; thrilled when he threatened, I'll get you next time; knowing he never would. He remembers his dad's smile; playing catch; making him run into the lake to catch the ball; hearing Josie's shrieks when he tossed her into the air; catching her; or letting her fall into the water, her loving it, her wanting more. He remembers his dad's laughter and feeling, for the first time, it was safe to scream and run and fall and be silly and get dirty and to keep on going even when the smells of too-much lake and sun and sand oozed from his skin. It was safe to have fun because his dad was having fun.

But then they stopped going to the lake and his dad stopped being fun.

"Well, let's do it," his mother says, bringing him back to the present, reminding him why they're here. "It must be time."

Josie checks her watch. "It's only six-twenty-nine; we have eight minutes yet."

"The sun is already setting," Matthew informs her. "We don't have to wait to exactly six-thirty-seven, for godsake!"

"He said sunset," she tells him. "And sunset is officially at six thirty-seven."

"It'll be dark then. Let's do it now when there's still light."

But they're silenced by their mother who's dumping the contents of a large baggie into the lake. They watch with open mouths as fine particles of ash and bone fall into the water. She jiggles the bag to get everything out, then drops the bag into the lake. Four feet below, the remains of Norman Billingston rock gently on the surface of Willow Lake, then lap against the wooden posts, which has the effect of folding him into the water—like sugar being folded into cookie dough. The process is slow and hypnotic and he can't take his eyes away.

Josie finally breaks the spell. "Shouldn't we say something?"

No one responds.

Across the lake, the sun is sinking into the trees, bordered by a pale yellow light that hugs the edge of the world. In minutes it has slipped below the horizon, taking that pale light with it.

"We have to go," his mother tells them, turning toward the parking lot. "This is ridiculous. I don't know why he did this to me."

Matthew takes in the growing darkness, the stillness, the chill of the lake, the rustle of dying leaves. "Because he felt like a kid here," he murmurs, mostly to himself.

"What?" she demands.

"Because he was happy here—feeling like a kid; maybe for the first time in his life. Free. Maybe that's why."

No one seems to agree, but Matthew is sure he's right. They head back to their cars, except for Josie who hasn't moved and seems to be searching for something in the water below. He goes back and touches her shoulder, which startles her. When she sees who it is, she leans into him and they comfort each other. Then, holding hands, they head back to their cars, stumbling on ruts and stones they can't see in the dark, facing the snap of a northwest wind and the promise of snow.

Ethan Marxhausen

The Family Lemonade

Please, someone, let me ask another question
that's sticking in my molars like a lemon:
I just rewrote some sections of my bible.
Revised but still a tiny bit too slippery,
elusive, still possessing old attraction.
A lost contact.

We're in the bathroom, taking out our contacts.
They shrivel in the saline like a question:
What was our mantra? and what was the attraction?
I squint, as if assaulted by the lemon.
The surface—as before—is just as slippery.
I check my Bible.

A page is missing from the family Bible
we realize, and set aside our contacts,
our fingers on the pages, stiff and slippery
searching for the answer to an ancient question:
to make a lemonade, how many lemons?
We break the old attraction.

For lemonade has always held a strange attraction
and with a sip we set aside our Bible
and freshly squeeze another piece of lemon
into the waiting bucket for our contacts,
now clear enough to ask another question—
why is the mind so slippery?

Now everything becomes a little slippery.
Our mother's lemonade has lost attraction.
The net result is still another question
to help construct our own Jefferson Bible.
The proofreader in our brain is making contact.
He feeds us lemons.

I've fallen out of love with all these lemons,
and other citrus fruits are just as slippery.
As water from the bucket soaks our contacts,
rebellion forms the basis of attraction.
Your recipe is just another bible
that gave me all the cause I had to question.

We're out of contact with the old attractions.
We hate the taste of lemon, but still it's slippery
and squirts our bible pages, dripping questions.

Linda Back McKay

Regrets

Rather than a sudden drop at dream's end
I'd like to be winked awake by pink
the dream finding its own conclusion
the honk of geese
washboard percussion
the ringing bell of sex or
even death, that low gong
trailing off into endless.

Rather than green as surety
I'd like a bifurcated tree branch
a suggestion of orange
translated from sunset
woven with scars
ghostly babies
born of bad choices
in and of themselves, holy.

Rather than blue (robin egg sky)
I'd like the red protection of roses
the new and the faded
each one a face
someone I may have known
or should have known,
someone who might have
kept me out of traffic
and in flight, high above
the power lines that transmit
all the power somewhere.

Travis Moore

Moon

It's hard to talk emotional immunity to the moon
or anything celestial that's always got its head down.
But did you hear his buffalo gals had to get jobs
teaching slow-dance-for-teens down at the Metro-Rec?
I'd weep too, pirouettes are animations specifically for the
    dark.

I don't expect lunar tears to fill much more than a nun's
    palm or the breadth of dusk.
But if he realizes he lost his sense of momma to the
    promise of science back in 69,
and that he missed the little innocent glass of milk spilling
    on the toes
of the birthday boy trying to be so quiet in the dark,
we'll all be offering double palms for the eclipsing soak.

(I won't mention the little boy's inquiring every kitchen
    corner
why falling stars listen to his whispered *go*,
and wave on the way out like heaven is a dream worth
    leaving.
We haven't got enough ocean for tear strain like that.)

The moon seems versed in the silent sigh but he speaks up
    like most
when the women stop dancing:
        "Promise me you'll take up the fiddle, for hope's sake,"

But I can't make guarantees of buffalo gals coming out to
    dance
when their motivations evolved from moonlight fox trots
to the promotional upgrade of a chaperoning mother:
making room for Jesus between the Stacies and Dans in
    gymnasium noir.

They'll all go corporate eventually anyway
and start organizing picnics for the youth,
more money that way—
Little black dresses become blue-collar slacks
and a tick-mark in the lineage of class is secured,
and when toddlers wonder about your wane and gain
the gals will shrug it out,
    "That's how God wanted it,"
never giving you another cosmic thought
my holy crescent cradle to telescope wants.

But we all know NASA went bankrupt over you,
and you didn't even get a complementary sweater
or a bobby pin that proved you've been
a shine on the entire neighborhood—

Can you even do an easy roll to China anymore?
Those sad pandas need your jungle illumine proof:
that all of this really IS necessary to jungle fodder,
that a roll in the hay and a tag-along morning
is just one hemisphere away, or in other words,
half a million migrations left to count.

So here's to you moon man you, I've been looking
for a light home since I dropped my eye from the sky.
I'll raise my tumbler of dusk to every irradiated bridge;
there you were, here you are.

I'll pour a sifter of star drip for you, too,
last justified creeper of the world;
go on and illuminate the lovers marking their backs
in the milkweed on daddy's back forty, I won't tell,
just as long as you make me a promise:

glow me a true cowboy
when I'm done crying to my momma
for being a man in the slaughter house,
wailing like a vagrant for you:
my last lantern in the wide cellar.

Kristine Price

Fine is Gone

The old Queen Anne had
doors like ghosts that lined the hallways;
thin tall soldiers at their posts watching all
in silence.

Where the hall formed an elbow a nook was tucked.
High above the street I looked at little ant people
who couldn't move and couldn't touch

and waited for you to come home.

Armies of mice ran the wallboards at night—sharp-
toed families all the night long scuttled down in rodent
chains, looking for crumbs in the cupboards.

Everyone was looking for something.

You were the sideshow who read Chaucer and Dylan,
named the constellations, played Beethoven and
talked about going to places like Russia;

nothing like the other mothers.

At first, a stab at decor. You painted the bedrooms
in seashore colors, lined the drawers and cupboards in paper,

hung a fancy picture over the mantel, the one with the
lady playing piano in a long, green gossamer gown.

But someone had to win that house and one day, the mice
had done it. The cat my sister dragged home still chased

them, but even the dog stopped raising her head.

Like tumbling twins you fell down quickly,
you and the old house we moved to far across town,
both so fine, so long.

But fine is gone; the thin bone china's cracked in two.
Limoges sold for pennies in yard sales while you drank with
people you never used to,

laughed at jokes you once called coarse,

lapped up the tongue of the man with you,
a dark-haired man with a wife across town who wouldn't know
Russia from Timbucktoo.

The silent soldier doors in the hall said nothing
when you and your friends crept past them,
finished your party in the silk of your room,
and me there waiting for you to come home.

There goes the crystal, there went the silver.
Legacies sold in a bust
down the river.

Fine is gone
it's ground in the Bayer I gave you tonight with a glass
of cold water.

Fine is gone,
sent her things packing,

fled on the dark black ribbon of night,

rode like a thief in the night on her carpet with cupboards
  and drawers,
everything in them, the woman, the house, the
children beneath it.

Julebukking

(Yool-a-booking)

The dog barked a frenzied welcome. Tia Fiskum pulled back the gingham curtain and peeked outside. "I can't see who it is." Tia scraped frost with her thumbnail.

Unexpected visitors were rare. Tia had a sinking feeling that it might be another visit from Pastor Husvedt about Norman's drinking. Dear God, she prayed. Anything but that.

Tia could tell Ma was nervous by the way she bit her lip. Maybe Ma worried about a preacher's visit, too. The kerosene lantern sputtered on the table, the evening shadows filling the corners of the old farm house. Norman swallowed his last bite of cake.

"It's too late for the Watkins man," Ma said.

Someone knocked on the door. Tia heard giggles and stomping feet. Norman pushed away from the table, his bib overalls stained from fixing the old tractor. "I'll get it."

Two people dressed as trolls stood in the doorway. The taller wore an old buffalo coat with swirling black curls. A feed sack draped over his face with cut-out eyes and nose beneath a tall pointy hat. The other, smaller by a foot, huddled beneath a horse-hide blanket and wore a carved wooden mask. They carried straw baskets shaped like goats. Their breath puffed vapors of cloud as they shifted their feet to keep warm, hunching their shoulders against the east wind.

"Julebukkers!" Ma motioned them into the kitchen with a delighted chuckle.

"Welkommen!" Ma's face lightened and she more resembled the woman Tia remembered from her childhood.

Tia relaxed. It was only foolery, something done between Christmas and New Years, an ancient Nordic custom that went back to the days of Thor.

"Who could you be?" Ma hurriedly cleared the table. "And on such a cold night."

Ma kept asking questions. "East wind means snow, don't you think?" Tia knew it was the old way—asking questions until one of the visitors answered. A voice was hard to disguise in a small community.

Tia fed a chunk of wood into the range and adjusted the damper. It had been a long while since anyone had come Julebukking—before the war at least. She remembered being afraid of the costumed neighbors—and her relief when her parents guessed who they were and the masks came off. Usually the Julebukkers took someone along from every place. By the end of the night, large groups traveled house to house.

Most of all, Tia remembered the laughter over coffee and lunch afterward, a vivid image of her father's face framed in lamplight. Such happiness they had shared before Pa died, before the war, before Norman was prisoner, before Clyde married Vera. Not like now. Nothing like now.

Tia filled the coffee pot from the water bucket.

These Julebukkers didn't fall for the old bait. They kept silent. The taller stood at a gawky angle, holding his arms away from his body in an ape-like manner. The shorter brayed like a donkey.

"Tia, can you guess who they are?" Ma said.

Before Tia could answer, Norman cut in, "I'd know you anywhere, Clyde Hanson, even without hearing the engine of your new Ford. Your big feet give you away every time."

Tia felt the blood drain from her face. She had thought it was Bertha Olson and her son, Julius. Clyde and Vera removed their masks. Envy, like a choking hand, cut off Tia's voice.

Tia busied herself getting lunch. She pulled a crock of rosettes, crispy fried cookies, from the top cupboard. Clyde loved rosettes and always made a big deal about Tia's being the best in the township. She hesitated. Clyde deserved only plain ginger cookies—or none at all. But Tia would not be rude to their newly-married neighbors. She dusted the rosettes with a layer of sugar and arranged them on the good cookie plate—the same as always.

Vera barely came up to Clyde's chin. Tia watched Vera's feet, small and dainty, pull from the big overshoes of her costume. As she looked away, Tia saw that Norman was watching Vera, too. He wore an unmistakable look of longing.

She and her brother made a good pair, Tia thought and swallowed the hard lump in her throat. She and Norman; Mr. and Miss Fiskum. Forever the bachelor and old maid. Tia loomed like a giant next to Vera. As soon as she set the table, Tia tucked her hands behind her back.

"Sit and have coffee," Ma said.

Clyde ate five rosettes, almost the whole plate. "These are delicious," he said and hooked another one with his index finger. "Vera, you need this recipe."

A warm flush crept up Tia's neck and cheeks as she stirred sugar into her coffee cup.

"Come with us," Clyde said. "We're going to all the neighbors."

Tia frantically searched for reasons to stay home. There was mending. She was reading a good book. The last thing she wanted was to parade through the neighborhood with Clyde and Vera.

"Please," Vera said, "We'll have fun."

"I'm too old for such foolishness," Ma said. "It's for young people."

"I've things to do," Tia said. "But you should go, Norman."

"Only if you go along," Norman said.

They all looked at her. Ma gave that encouraging nod she always used when she wanted Tia to do something against her will. Vera's face lit up like a Christmas tree. Tia supposed Vera hoped they would become best of friends.

Tia didn't need another friend. But Norman did. Since he had returned from the war, Norman had changed. Maybe the old custom would be good for him. Tia would do anything to help her brother. It was good of Clyde to think of it.

She finally nodded and Ma flurried to gather costumes.

Ma pulled a shirt from the mending basket and helped Tia into an old pair of bib overalls that had belonged to her father. They fit her well, not too long or tight. Norman handed her a wool cap. With the ear flaps pulled down and the cap's bill tugged forward, identification was impossible. Ma helped Tia into men's work gloves and then into

Norman's barn boots. Vera suggested she tie a bandanna handkerchief over her mouth like a cowboy.

"Swell!" Vera clapped her hands. "You look like the Lone Ranger."

"You'll fool them," Clyde said. "They'll never guess."

Ma fished in the closet for her oldest dress. It hung on Norman, tight across the shoulders but covered his legs down to his feet. Ma tied an apron around his waist. Norman pulled on a bulky barn coat, swathed his face and head in a wool scarf and topped it with Pa's old fur hat.

"All you need is lipstick." Clyde elbowed Norman in the ribs.

Ma's eyes glittered. "Have fun," she said.

Tia hurried to the Ford parked behind the lilac bushes. She crawled into the back seat, expecting Norman to follow. Instead, Vera scrambled in beside her.

"We gals will sit in the back so we can gab," Vera said. "The men need the leg room."

Tia's legs crowded against the seat. She scrunched to the side trying to fit her legs at an angle.

A million stars winked above them and a half moon waned. Headlights reflected on drifted snow. Their breathing steamed the inside of the windows as the heater battled the bitter cold.

"Good God," Norman said. "You could have picked a warmer night."

"Your Ma's right about snow moving in," Clyde said. "It was tonight or never." Then Clyde entertained them for the first cold mile by telling how he woke up to a gnawing sound and discovered a porcupine eating the machine shed.

"The dog finally went after it," Vera said, "got his mouth full of quills." Her voice trembled. "It was terrible."

"Any damage to your shed?" Tia said.

They talked back and forth about buildings and hazards to them. Vera told how her father had once driven through the wall of a garage when he was drunk. Conversation lagged.

"Any porcupines in Germany?" Clyde said.

Tia held her breath. Norman avoided all questions about his time in the Nazi POW camp. A heavy silence filled the car.

"Never saw any." Norman finally said. "A few squirrels. Birds."

Tia let out her breath with a sigh. It was good for Norman to be out with people, even if they had to dress up as fools to do it.

The feeble gleam from the dashboard cast an eerie light in the car. At least she could hide in the darkness of the back seat where Clyde couldn't see her. She could look at the back of his curly head all she wanted without him knowing. She had always admired the curls around his ears.

"Before we get to the Olson's," Vera said from her side of the backseat, "we'd like to ask you and Norman something." She had that child-like look on her face that Tia had grown to expect. "Do you want to ask them, Clyde?" Her voice sounded breathless and hesitant, as if unsure of his response.

"Go ahead," Clyde said.

"My sister, Selma, lives in California," Vera said, "or we'd ask her." She fiddled with the carved mask on her lap, scraping a sliver away from the cheek. "We're expecting, you know," she said. "We'd like you and Norman to stand as godparents."

Norman's jaw dropped open. Tia's heart sank to her shoes. She had dreamed of standing at the altar with Clyde—but never as godmother for his child. A mental image of them together at the baptismal fount skittered through her mind. Standing exposed before the whole church, fueling the gossip about her broken heart. Of taking responsibility for Clyde's child although he had fallen for a town girl. Tia's throat turned dusty and she doubted she could answer even if she had words to speak.

"I'm not much of a Lutheran," Norman said with a gruff voice from the passenger side of the front seat. "Not too much of anything, I guess."

"I can think of no one better," Clyde said and his voice carried none of the usual teasing banter. "We've been friends since diapers and our parents before us. You and Tia are like brother and sister to me."

"Please say yes, Tia." Vera clasped mittened hands in front of her.

Tia thought again how Vera looked like Shirley Temple waiting for applause. Vera cared more for their dog's mouth than the new shed. She was only a child. Not sensible enough to be a mother.

What did Clyde see in her?

"We'll think about it," Norman said at last.

Tia sent a silent thank you to her brother, mental telepathy though it was. Emotion clogged her throat, robbed her of breath, and stopped speech.

"Don't know I'll stay in this country," Norman said. "I've been thinking about moving on."

The road was an icy track with soft drifts of snow gathered in the curves. Across Olson's field, the snow mounded like ocean waves, whipped by the wind. Snow fences stretched across the western lip of the road in a futile effort to keep the road open.

"Selma says California is warm and sunny year round," Vera said.

"Don't start with that again," Clyde said.

Norman started to say something but the car turned into the Olson driveway.

"Time to put on your mask, Kemo Sabe," Clyde said and stopped the Ford a short way from the Olson's door. He pulled the hand brake and turned out the headlights. "Tonto and Lone Ranger are Julebukking tonight!"

Old Lady Olson greeted them in her bedclothes, her white hair loosed from its crown and falling down to her waist, holding the lantern high to get glimpses of their faces.

"Julebukkers!" she said and burst into a toothless smile. "Uff da! Come in out of the cold wind."

They stood on newspapers. Clyde took the same ape-like stance he had used at their house, standing with his elbows cocked and shoulders hunched. Vera looked like a little kid behind the carved mask while Tia towered at her side. Norman made an unlikely woman with his wide shoulders and stubbly chin.

"George Carlson, is that you?" Mrs. Olson poked Tia in the arm. "I know it's you." She reached to hug Tia. "Welcome home, George. I hadn't heard you were back."

Tia shook her head and pulled back, humiliated beyond description. No one would ever mistake Vera Hanson for a man.

"Tall strapping boy." Mrs. Olson chortled with happiness. "I'd know you anywhere! When did you get home?"

Norman unwrapped the scarf around his face. "It's just us, Mrs. Olson," he said in a flat, soft voice. "Clyde and Vera and Tia and me."

Tia gave him a grateful glance and he nodded his head to show he understood. They had always been close. At least until he went away to war. It was as if her brother left for war and a stranger came home wearing his face.

"Norman!" Vera said. "You spoiled it. She wasn't even close!"

"Stand on the rug and I'll get your drinks." Mrs. Olson placed the lamp on the edge of the table and rummaged in her cupboard until she pulled out a wine decanter. "This will warm you!"

Mrs. Olson's chokecherry wine was widely acclaimed throughout Tolga Township. Norman's eyes lit with anticipation.

"Julius will be sorry he missed you," Mrs. Olson said as she poured the wine into thimble sized glasses. "He went to a picture show. Something with Spencer Tracy and Katherine Hepburn."

"Don't mind if I do." Norman reached for a glass.

"Nothing too good for our soldiers," Mrs. Olson said. "So glad you're home safe and sound. I suppose you're going to take over your ma's farm."

Norman ignored her question and downed the wine as Mrs. Olson passed the glasses to the rest of them and then refilled Norman's.

"Your ma must be glad you made it home all right," she continued. "Will you be adding to your herd? The price of milk is up."

Norman did not answer. Clyde stuck out his empty glass, too, and then Norman held his out for another refill. Mrs. Olson motioned toward Vera and Tia but they shook their heads.

Tia had a hard time emptying her glass. Since Norman's return from the war, his drinking had caused Tia more than a little heartache. Enough that she considered joining the Women's Temperance Union and giving up on liquor altogether.

"We used to go Julebukking," Mrs. Olson said. "All the Hultgren's and the Swenson's. We made our own fun."

If Julius had been home, no doubt they would have taken him along, but not Mrs. Olson already in her nightgown. Instead, they said their goodnights and trudged out to the car. The cold a bitter slap after the warmth of the kitchen.

"Another for the road?" Norman pulled a flat bottle from his pocket and held it out to Clyde. "Might as well take a nip."

"I'm driving," Clyde said. "Maybe the girls want some."

"None for me," Vera said and patted her stomach.

Norman did not offer any to Tia. Instead he tipped the bottle and guzzled a long swallow. Tia wondered where he found money for liquor. They needed every cent to pay their mortgage. A sharp anger rose up within her, anger at Norman for bringing a bottle along, anger at herself for being unable to stop his great thirst.

"Nosy old bitch." Norman took another swig from the bottle. "None of her business what I do. None of anyone's damn business. "

"She didn't mean nothing," Vera said.

They visited all the houses in the neighborhood. Many gave nips of apricot brandy or homemade wine. Norman loosened up the more he drank. He was almost staggering by the time they arrived at the Hansels.

"Hansels are next," Clyde said. "Think we can squeeze Millie into the car with us?"

"Good old Millie," Norman said with a slur. "Sent me cookies while I was a P.O.W."

No one said anything. Tia wanted to slump under the seat.

They fitted their masks in the yard as the dog circled and barked.

"It's all right," Tia said and reached out to pat the dog. "Good girl." She and Mildred had been friends since they were babies. The dog knew her well.

Clarence opened the door and ushered them into the kitchen. Clyde postured and Norman stood like Betty Grable with his chest stuck out and hip pushed forward. Vera brayed like a donkey and Tia wanted only to melt away like the frost on the windows.

The sound of piano music abruptly ended as Mildred joined them. The kitchen was homey with its warm electric lights and gas range. Tia felt the dryness of her skin. Like the Sahara, like a California desert.

"Julebukkers!" Mildred said. "Don't mind your overshoes."

Clarence eyed them for a long moment and then scowled at Norman. "Norman Fiskum."

"How did you guess?" Vera said. "He has a great costume!"

"Should I fetch the brandy, Father?" Mildred said.

Clarence shook his head. "Looks like they've had enough."

Tia felt her heart drop. Clarence was on the Church Board. The community had been tolerant of Norman's behavior. It couldn't last.

Mildred put the coffee on the stove and pulled cookies from a stone jar.

"Will you come with us, Millie?" Vera said.

Mildred started to answer when Clarence interrupted.

"Not tonight." Clarence sat with his arms folded across his chest. "We've plans for tonight."

Mildred looked in surprise.

"I'm driving," Clyde said. "Mildred would be fine with us."

"Not tonight," Clarence said. "Another time."

The talk switched to hog prices, the cost of seed corn, and the snowy forecast verified by the easterly wind. Mildred kept cups filled. Tia asked Mildred about the Luther League social coming up. Vera prattled about a new motion picture she wanted to see.

Finally Clyde pushed away from the table and everyone stood.

"Sure you don't want to come, Mildred?" Tia asked.

Mildred looked toward her father and shrugged one shoulder while Tia shook her head.

"We'll talk tomorrow," Mildred said to Tia. "Have fun."

"Good old Millie," Norman said when they were back in the car. "Her dad won't let her out with a killer. Folks are like that, you know. Sent us off to kill Nazis but when we come back, they look down on us."

"Norman," Tia said. "That's enough."

"Don't be too hard on Clarence," Clyde said. "Ed didn't come back you know."

"Ain't my fault." Norman drank again from the bottle.

"Where next?" Tia said. She had to turn it around somehow. If she said the right words, it would all turn out all right. "The Hegdahls?"

"First the Carlson's." Clyde turned the wheel sharply to avoid an unexpected rut in the icy road. The tires slipped and Vera squealed. "For goodness sake, Vera," Clyde said. "I'm a good driver. There's nothing to worry about."

Tia wished with all her might that she had stayed home. She didn't like being with Clyde and Vera, didn't care to see them squabble over petty things, and didn't like the side of Clyde she was seeing. He had grown bossy.

"Vera," Norman said with a slurred voice. "Tell me about California."

Vera chattered as Norman emptied his bottle, rolled down the window and threw it out into the ditch. Clyde didn't say anything, just pulled a fag from his pocket and lit it with the lighter.

"Damn Germans!" Norman said. "They'll never change." Norman leaned against the car door and groaned. "Damn them all to hell—and the Nips."

"Norman," Vera said.

Norman groaned louder.

"Be quiet, Vera!" Clyde said. "Do you want me to stop, Norman? Are you going to be sick? Don't be sick in our new car."

"I'm sick of the Germans. Sick of this God-forsaken country." Without warning Norman threw up. Vomit spewed over the dashboard, the car door and the front of Norman's coat.

Clyde smashed on the brakes, parked the car, and leapt out his door and ran around and opened Norman's door. He grabbed Norman by his arm and pulled him out, just as another wave of vomiting occurred.

"Good God!" Clyde said. "You could have told me to stop."

Norman lay in the snow, slobbering and crying. "Nosy bitch. It's none of her business what I do. I'll farm if I want, or leave if I want, God damn her."

Clyde wiped off the dashboard and the seat with handfuls of soft snow, cursing under his breath, while Vera knelt by Norman's side and wiped his face with her handkerchief. Tia stepped out of the car, overwhelmed with helplessness.

"I'll leave if I want to," Norman said.

"That's right," Vera said. "No one can force you to do anything."

Tia felt tears roll down her face. "I think it's time we call it a night."

"But what about the Carlson's and the Hegdahl's?" Vera said. "It's too early to quit now."

Doris Lueth Stengel

Arrival & Departure

I drive with my father to the small town where my
grandfather settled when he arrived in America over a
century ago.

farmland black as coal
banked on the grate of freedom
warmth for newcomers

Here among other German immigrants he practiced his craft
of carpentry, cupboards and chests carved with twining vines,
polished to buttery hue. Builder of coffins, he buried the dead.

far away from home
no familiar forests
grass horizons grass

My uncle was the only son to remain in this fertile landscape.
Now we travel to visit him as his health fails. He a short man
beside my father's height. Both speak terse male love.

sailing overhead
gentle breath of death catches
dry leaves in tree tops

Hands in pockets they stand and talk. Not saying the things they
both know. Behind them the stacked rock garden, my aunt's
pride. Uncle already looks past us at horizons we cannot see.

hardwork background of rock
plans caught in the crevices
future under stone

When I Was Six in Silver Spring

I stood on the stairs looking at Daddy's photo on the wall, trying hard to remember him. The man in the picture seemed like a stranger. I had not seen my father for almost a year. It was 1942 and I was six.

Immediately after the Japanese bombed Pearl Harbor on December 7, 1941, my father was called to Washington. Months earlier, with war imminent, Congress had passed a bill enacting rationing into law, but legal jargon needed to be translated into language that business people and shopkeepers, who would implement the laws, could understand. My father, a small town lawyer, had been recommended for the task.

As thousands of workers poured into the Capitol to fill newly created jobs, a critical housing shortage developed. Daddy had been working in Washington almost a year before he was able to find a house big enough for our family of six. In October 1942, he found the place he was looking for in Silver Spring, Maryland. My mother, three siblings and I boarded a train in Fergus Falls, Minnesota, and arrived in Washington three days later. Through the window I scanned the crowds to catch sight of my father waiting on the station platform.

"Daddy, Daddy," I screamed as I hugged his cushioned girth and felt his comforting presence. Mother threw her arms around him, her face against his shoulder as he held her. We retrieved our luggage from big wooden carts, then Daddy loaded the bags into a borrowed car; we climbed in and headed for home.

He pulled up in front of a modest house on Grace Church Road in Silver Spring, Maryland, a quiet old town just outside the District of Columbia, with wide grassy boulevards and huge old trees shading nineteenth century homes. The house Daddy had rented welcomed us with its wraparound porch and large lawn.

We immediately made friends with the family whose back yard lay behind ours on the opposite side of a thicket of shrubbery. Their daughter Joan was my older sister Katherine's age, and her brother Bruce a little younger than me. We four became the hub of the neighborhood gang. Their street marked the edge of town. Beyond it stood a large expanse of woods with a dry creek bed and railroad tracks running through it.

While settling into our new home, my parents temporarily hired a motherly black woman named Marie to help unpack our things and care for my baby brother. Dishes and other breakable items arrived packed in excelsior inside wooden barrels, which Marie unpacked and placed on the front porch. One morning my brother Butch, a bit of a pyromaniac at four and a half, was playing alone on the porch while Mother and Marie worked inside. No one had seen him take matches from the kitchen and tuck them into his pocket.

He soon discovered that the barrels, half filled with excelsior, made a great place to play. He climbed inside a barrel next to the front door and struck a match against the rough wood. The small lick of flame ignited the wood shavings. Maybe it was a faint scent of sulfur or a tiny curl of smoke next to the open front door. Perhaps it was woman's intuition, but something alerted Marie to danger. She sprang out the front door just in time to see a fire starting in the barrel of excelsior, with Butch in the middle.

In a flash she lifted him out, ran inside and returned with a kettle of water to douse the flames before more damage could be done. Fire had scorched the painted wood siding. My parents were forever thankful to Marie for saving not only Butch but the house. Marie became our respected household helper, always welcome in our home. She came occasionally to help with housework and child care.

After school we roamed the neighborhood, exploring the nearby woods and creek and looking for hobo camps along the railroad tracks, with Katherine and Joan as our leaders. One day we noticed a pear tree across the wide green lawn next door, seemingly a long distance away. We had never seen anyone going in or out of the house, almost as if no one lived there. If that were the case, no one would care if we climbed the pear tree. Within a few minutes children were among the branches, vying to see who could climb the highest or command the best view.

I was scared, but I wanted to be part of the gang. I hated being timid and didn't want people to think I was a sissy, so I put on my bold and daring act. We were so absorbed in our escapade we didn't notice a woman walking across the lawn toward us.

"Get down from that tree immediately!" she ordered. In an instant everyone but me was on the ground running away. I remained frozen in place, standing on a branch while clinging to the tree trunk, afraid either to jump or climb down. Humiliated and miserable, I took the brunt of her scolding before she helped me down; then I raced off as fast as I could. Wanting to be with the older kids, I reluctantly went along with their nervy schemes, always the one who got caught.

Platoons of uniformed soldiers occasionally marched in formation down Columbia Boulevard. We could hear them singing at the tops of their voices before they reached the corner of Grace Church Road—Over There ... Anchors Away ... From the Halls of Montezuma—another reminder that our country was at war. Children ran along beside them while neighbors stood on the boulevard waving and cheering.

During air raid drills everyone was required to black out their windows at night so no light could be seen. Air raid wardens frequently went door to door checking for light. Mother was embarrassed about nine o'clock one evening when a warden rang our doorbell. "Madam, your attic light is on!" He reprimanded her. Someone had gone to the attic that day and forgotten to turn the light off, a major infraction. She apologized profusely.

If enemy bombers had reached the Capitol, even one light would have created a target. Such carelessness was inexcusable. In 1942 real patriotism, beyond mere flag waving, was crucial. The goal of winning the war demanded wholehearted support from everyone. It wasn't enough just to save tin cans, paper, tin foil, string and rubber bands, or to buy U.S. War Bonds and Savings Stamps. We needed to be prepared for possible attack by enemy forces.

Soon after we moved to Maryland in October we began anticipating Aunt Marge, Uncle Jack and my eleven-year-old cousin Mary joining us for Christmas. Mary was small for her age with brown hair and eyes, lively and talkative, with a great sense of adventure. She was a tiny whirlwind with a reputation for getting in trouble, in contrast with tall, blond, reticent me, staying quietly in the background.

Mother and her sister hadn't seen each other for a whole year. When they arrived on Christmas Eve afternoon, Aunt Marge's booming voice and loud laughter resonated through the house as everyone exchanged greetings. Mother showed off the baby, John, now eleven months old, as Mary jumped up and down with excitement. Aunt Marge and Mother disappeared into the kitchen to visit as they worked on preparations for the Christmas Eve Smorgasbord.

Uncle Jack settled into a big chair in the living room with a book. Daddy arrived home from his long hours of work in the Capitol just in time for the smorgasbord, feeling fortunate to have Christmas Day off. Mary, Katherine and I called for Joan and Bruce to come out and play. "Let's go down to the woods!" Joan said. "We can show your cousin the hobo camp!"

"Sounds like fun! Let's go!" Mary shouted. We were intrigued by the woods a block from our back yard. A path ran beside a dry creek bed where we climbed huge boulders and enormous roots of old trees. Half burned logs and warm ashes alerted us to a recently abandoned hobo camp. Logs surrounded the fire, and empty tin cans and bottles were scattered about. But it was a far more dangerous place to play than we realized.

The hobos, homeless unemployed men who needed food, a place to sleep, and a chance to find work, regularly rode the rails. They hopped off and on trains as they came through, knocked on doors asking for work or food, then moved on. But we did not see any hobos that day.

After exploring the creek bed we climbed to the top of a high railroad embankment. As we walked along the tracks, we heard a train whistle in the distance. When it began to sound ominously close, Mary yelled, "I'm getting out of here!" She hunkered down on her haunches and began to slide down the steep bank, feet under her, cinders and gravel flying. Dislodged stones bounced around her like flying missiles.

Everyone else was too scared to move. Suddenly Mary hit something in her path, flipped over and tumbled down the rest of the embankment head first, hitting her head on a railroad tie at the bottom. She was knocked out cold. Everyone but me scrambled down after her. Paralyzed at the top, I was too terrified to do anything but sit at the far outer edge of the rail bed, holding on as tightly as I could.

By then the train was barely crawling. As it came even with me, the engineer leaned his head out the open window and scolded, "Hey you, little girl! You shouldn't be playing here. You could get hurt! Go on home and don't play here again!" I looked at the engineer above me and said nothing as I clung to the top of the embankment, rigid with fear. He needn't have warned me away. There was no possibility I would ever go near those tracks again.

The others made it to the bottom without falling. I have no memory of how I got down. Mary regained consciousness and opened her eyes just as Katherine, posing theatrically with her hands on her hips announced, "She's dead!" But Mary was definitely alive, although woozy, with a lump on her forehead and a throbbing headache. Her arms were scratched and smudged with black streaks. There was a rip in the seat of her new corduroy trousers, now filthy with soot.

Slowly we made our way home, helping Mary along. We slipped into the house through the back door. Mary moaned as she eased into a kitchen chair and put her head down on the table. Her mother looked at her and shrieked with alarm, "Mary! Oh no! What happened?" Uncle Jack put a cold wet cloth on her forehead and gave her an aspirin with a glass of water, while Katherine explained how Mary had fallen and hit her head, not mentioning anything about hobos or a train. Mary spent Christmas Eve curled up in a big chair in the living room, wrapped in a blanket. The rest of the family exchanged gifts and enjoyed our traditional smorgasbord.

On Christmas morning we opened our stockings. There were no chocolate Santas that year, as no chocolate could be found anywhere except for the armed forces. We each received a candy cane, apples, walnuts, colored pencils or crayons and a small toy. Later in the day we began preparing for Christmas dinner. Mother had made a centerpiece of small, red lighted candles floating in a crystal bowl of water in the middle of the dining room table. To make them, she had melted down old candle stubs, poured the wax into small fluted Jell-O molds, and added a wick. They looked festive floating in the crystal bowl.

Then Uncle Jack and Aunt Marge began rehashing a long-standing argument over the question, does hair burn? Uncle Jack could be stubborn and overbearing, telling his wife for years that hair doesn't burn. She always insisted, "Don't be ridiculous, of course hair burns." Finally Uncle Jack decided to prove he was right.

He picked up a candle from the bowl and held the flame to the top of his head before anyone could stop him. I remember standing in the dining room staring at the bizarre scene as a smudge of smoke appeared above his head and the acrid smell of burning hair filled the room. Everyone stood aghast as Aunt Marge jumped up to reach the top of his head with her hand, shouting "Jack! Jack!" She quickly extinguished his smoldering hair with a few slaps to the top of his head. For decades afterward, whenever Uncle Jack got a little too sure of himself, Aunt Marge would say, "Yes, and hair doesn't burn."

That Christmas we didn't see any hobos, but a few months later, on Easter Sunday, we were eating breakfast in the dining room when we were interrupted by a knock on a door that opened from the dining room to the wraparound porch. We were surprised because that door was rarely used, nor did we generally have visitors on Sunday morning. Mother opened it to find a shabby, unshaven older man. "Excuse me ma'am," he said, "could you please spare me something to eat?" Mother asked him to wait on the porch.

While we sat at our places around the table staring toward the door, Daddy went to the kitchen and made a big stack of pancakes with syrup, put them in a paper bag, and handed them to the man. He thanked us and went on his way. We watched out a window as he cut through the shrubbery in back, heading toward the woods and railroad tracks. I was happy we had shared our pancakes with a hobo.

Marie walked to our home from the small Negro settlement where she lived a few blocks away, which everyone called "The Nigger Hollow." Grace Church Road ended a couple of blocks past our house, where the neighborhood of dignified turn of the century houses with wide green lawns ended, and scrubby woods and brambles began. A narrow path cut through tall weeds for a few hundred yards or so, then into the woods, passing a ramshackle old house where "poor white trash" lived. Flimsy wire fencing enclosed a clay yard full of snarling dogs. Marie's neighborhood began farther along the path through the woods. One day as she walked home one of the dogs broke loose and attacked her, severely biting the back of her leg.

She was confined to bed, unable to walk. Mother made bean soup with ham for Marie's family and put it in quart canning jars with tight lids. Katherine, Butch and I delivered it to her home. It was difficult making our way through scrubby woods and overgrown brush, pushing branches out of our way to avoid being scratched by thorns. I remember creeping through the woods feeling frightened, hearing frantically barking dogs while staying as far away as possible from the poor white trash place.

Finally we came to a clearing where Marie's small unpainted house slumped behind a sagging porch; we crossed a hard-packed red clay yard and knocked on the screen door. A girl of about thirteen invited us inside. I saw Marie in a dark room lying on a sagging iron bed, loosely covered with shabby quilts. Several children stood silently in the gloomy background, looking at us with large, solemn dark eyes. "We brought you some soup," Katherine said, smiling. We stayed a few awkward minutes before leaving for home.

Our neighbors on Grace Church Road were appalled when they learned that we had brought soup to a colored family. They let us know it was unseemly for whites to get involved in the personal problems of Negroes. This was just not done in Silver Spring. But Marie had received no help from her white neighbor with the vicious dog, or anyone else we knew of.

My parents believed in expressing neighborliness and compassion. Daddy filed a law suit on Marie's behalf, asking the court to award damages, and won a judgment against the dog's owner. I doubt if Marie collected any money, but I know my parents stood up for what was right, and I believe they would have helped her financially as much as they were able. I wonder now if they had begun to feel out of place in Silver Spring.

That summer my parents bought a house in a new development nearby where people from all over the country had moved to work for the government. I began second grade in Landover Hills, Maryland, in the fall of 1943, but before Christmas Daddy was transferred to Fargo, where we lived until the war ended. We returned to Fergus Falls for my year of fifth grade, then moved to Minneapolis where I grew up as a true-blue Midwesterner.

Francine Marie Tolf

Souvenir

The old man hugged his chest tight
as he sucked on a cigarette outside the conservatory,
gaunt legs twisted around one another
like Picasso's blue guitar player.
Take his picture, I whispered to my boyfriend,
pretend it's the flowers. He did, and years later,
in an album full of grinning relatives,
a stranger whose limbs are lean
with sorrow, instructs me how those moments
we toss integrity to the wind
flutter back to us.

Burden of Man and Beast in the Common Life

O n their way upstairs from Morning Prayer, Father
Conrad asked Novice Jack to come into his office.
Jack sat in the straight-back chair because Sam
was occupying the La-Z-Boy. "Do you want to go for a
walk?" Jack asked the collie. Getting out of the recliner, Sam
wagged his tail in an affirmative response. "We'll go as soon
as I've had my breakfast," Jack told him. It was Novice Jack's
week to walk the dog.

"I have something to tell you," the novice master said
to Jack.

"This is meditation time," Jack reminded Father
Conrad. "Are you sure we should be talking now?"

"It will only take a minute."

"What have I done wrong?"

"I heard you call your classmate that name again
last evening. There, I've given you something to meditate
about—fraternal charity."

Father Conrad, however, often found himself being
unkind to the older novice. When the monks manifested
their faults every month at *culpa*, Father Conrad confessed,
"For being impatient with the novices." Many of the monks
presumed it was Novice Jeremiah who was the greater
burden for Father Conrad than Novice Jack who was the
younger novice by twenty years. Some of the monks were
even referring to Novice Jeremiah by the nickname bestowed
on him by his novitiate classmate. Others were advising
Father Conrad to send him packing.

After the bell for the Angelus had rung, Father Conrad went downstairs for breakfast. He took three pancakes and two sausages, one of each which he wrapped in a paper napkin for Sam. His two novices were the only ones at the table. Neither wished to converse with him. It was apparent to Father Conrad that Novice Jack was ticked off. The young man did not like being corrected. He was avoiding eye contact with Father Conrad, refusing to acknowledge the presence of his novice master. Novice Jeremiah ignored both of them. The portly novice didn't look up from his plate on which there was enough food to feed several people. Father Conrad had tried convincing Jeremiah to cut down, and had even threatened him with the imposition of a medically approved diet. The physician's report, submitted along with Jeremiah's application form, had indicated obesity. Upon his arrival at the monastery to begin the novitiate, the abbot told Father Conrad, "That man is grossly overweight. You'd better talk him into dieting."

After the novices left, Father Nathaniel came along and took the chair vacated by Jeremiah.

He whispered to Father Conrad, "I bet Lard Ass was sitting here. This chair is really heated up."

"Yes, that was Brother Novice Jeremiah's place."

Leaving the refectory together, Father Nathaniel asked the novice master, "What have you got tucked away in that napkin?"

"A treat for Sam."

"I might have known. Why don't you get rid of that dog? And that novice?"

*　　*　　*

Father Conrad requested Jeremiah to remain after the morning's novitiate class. "Are you really happy here?" he asked. "To me, you appear glum much of the time."

"Interior happiness is what counts. Not external."

"I suspect you have neither, Brother. It seems doubtful that you have a monastic vocation."

Father Conrad waited for a response from the novice, but Brother Jeremiah only stared at him.

"You should shed some weight. All that fat is unbecoming of an aspiring ascetic."

"It's the condition of my soul that counts. Not my body."

"You need more exercise."

"I take my turn walking the dog."

"How about carrying the twenty-five pound bags of dog food up to my room?"

"That's four flights of stairs."

"Exactly."

"Shouldn't Brother Jack also bear the burden?"

"No. He already gets plenty of exercise."

*   *   *

Angela Dunlop had entrusted Sam to Father Conrad when she moved off her farm and into an apartment in town. Most of the monks liked Sam. Only a few of them were annoyed with Father Conrad for having given the dog a new home. Abbot Anthony had warned him, "Don't let him become a nuisance." Although the abbot had insisted that the collie be kept outdoors, Father Conrad brought him inside when more and more of the monks objected to his barking at night. "He's only chasing the raccoons and rabbits out of the garden," Father Conrad said in defense of Sam. Nevertheless, it seemed like the prudent thing to bring the dog indoors at night so the monks' sleep wouldn't be disturbed. Now that it was July, Father Conrad left Sam in the building all the time so that he might benefit from the air conditioning. "And it is easier keeping him groomed this way," Father Conrad told Abbot Anthony. The dog was prevented from running through the fields and windbreaks, and Father Conrad didn't have to remove sticks, brambles, and pieces of wire from Sam's luxurious sable coat.

Sam had been at the monastery only a week longer than Jack and Jeremiah. All three of them arrived at the beginning of summer. Over the past few weeks, it occurred to Father Conrad that an analogy could be made between the novices and canines. Jack was like a puppy whose training required patient repetition. Jeremiah was similar to an old dog that simply couldn't be taught new tricks.

Soon after their clothing in the monastic habit, Abbot Anthony had asked Father Conrad to once more bring a certain matter to the attention of the younger novice.

"You'll have to take off that earring," Father Conrad instructed Brother Jack.

The novice touched the silver hoop piercing his left ear. "I do when I go to bed."

"The abbot doesn't want you wearing that thing. He thinks that someone called to monastic life should not adorn himself with jewelry. Wearing an earring is especially sissified, he says."

"The abbot wears a gold cross. And a ring, too, on his right hand."

"Well, yes he does. They are symbols of abbatial authority."

"I'd feel naked without my earring."

"Please! Remove the earring. This is the third time you've been requested to do so."

Jack was a good-looking lad of twenty who had dropped out of college to enter the monastery. Novices nowadays were usually older men who had abandoned careers in the world in order to become monks—men like Jeremiah. Jack had been a P.E. major at the State University and Father Conrad assured him that somewhere down the road he would have an opportunity to coach in the high school run by the monks. "Until then, Brother, please do not bounce the basketball in your room." That had been on Jack's second day at the monastery.

After graduating from a business college, Novice Jeremiah had worked in a bank for a good number of years—living at home with his mother all that time. Father Conrad was always suspicious of men who came to the monastery at Jeremiah's age. Why had they never married? Father Conrad knew what Abbot Anthony was hinting at when he said that wearing an earring made Novice Jack look sissified. "But lots of guys wear earrings nowadays," Jack insisted. "Some of them in both ears." There certainly was no evidence that Jack was gay. Nevertheless, Father Conrad also disapproved of the earring.

The novice master had definite misgivings about Jeremiah, however. "Do you like women?" Father Conrad had asked the older novice soon after his arrival at the monastery.

"I have never been in love."

"Not even once?"

"Mary. I will always love her."

"Who is she?"

"The mother of Jesus."

"Oh, yes. Of course." Father Conrad felt that the novice had purposely set this trap in order to embarrass him. "What I meant was, aside from loving your heavenly mother and the one you had here on earth, did you ever have a girlfriend?"

"There was a woman at the bank who was fond of me. I gave her a box of chocolates on St. Valentine's Day, and she responded so emotionally that you'd think I'd given her an engagement ring. Actually, I'd purchased the chocolates for Mother, but she died on February eighth."

"You didn't appreciate the fact that this woman showed affection for you?"

"I should have kept the chocolates and eaten them myself."

*   *   *

Abbot Anthony liked Sam. He was wondering, though, if perhaps Father Conrad had not been bringing the dog to the community room too often lately. Sometimes Sam made a nuisance of himself at recreation, especially on nights when the monks had popcorn. The collie went from monk to monk, placing his head in each one's lap, pleading with his big brown eyes for a handful of popcorn. It seemed to Abbot Anthony that an increasing number of the monks were telling the dog, "Get away" or "Stop begging."

It was not Sam, however, that Abbot Anthony had on his mind when he summoned the novice master to his office. "I'm glad to see that at last Brother Novice Jack has removed the earring."

"He disposed of it very reluctantly."

"It made him look like a sissy. You know what I mean?"

"Some young men these days wear them in both ears. Even those who aren't gay."

Abbot Anthony pounded the desk with his fist. "The boys in our high school cannot wear earrings. Why should someone who is aspiring to become a monk?"

"Well, anyway, he's finally submitted. I'm glad he did."

Abbot Anthony said, "Now, about that other novice."

Father Conrad was relieved the abbot had nothing else to say about Novice Jack. Earlier in the day, Father Conrad had told him to refrain from singing in the shower, to cease running in the corridors, to make his bed before noon, and to wipe the grin off his face at communal prayer. It would have been difficult facing Jack with one more thing that needed correction.

"What is your problem with Novice Jeremiah?" Father Conrad asked.

"You'll have to find some other work for him. Father Nathaniel wants him out of the library."

Finding work for Jeremiah was becoming a burden for Father Conrad. Sooner or later, the novice was dismissed from every work assignment given to him. It seemed no one in the monastery appreciated Brother Jeremiah's assistance.

"Why does Father Nathaniel no longer want him?" Father Conrad asked.

"Because Jeremiah removed books and burned them. Dumped the books into the incinerator and set a match to them. Works by authors he considers heretical—certain contemporary theologians. Books are so expensive nowadays. We shouldn't be burning them."

Father Conrad agreed, "We should not."

"The librarian is pretty upset. He told me, 'This is how old Adolph got his start—book burning.' He meant Adolph Hitler. Not Father Adolph."

"I understand that."

"The kitchen master says the novice is eating us out of house and home. Can't you curb that man's appetite?"

"I'll try harder."

"The liturgist is angry because Novice Jeremiah is always griping about our having abandoned Latin chant. It's coming back in some places he tells the liturgist."

"Novice Jeremiah is extremely conservative."

"He's a pain-in-the-ass," Abbot Anthony said.

*   *   *

As a punishment for having burned the library books, Father Conrad made the novice kneel on the refectory floor during the evening meal. With your arms outstretched," he told him. "You want to go back to the old ways. Well, here's an old-fashioned penance."

"When will I eat?"

"You won't. You'll go without supper tonight."

"May I go to the kitchen for leftovers later on?"

"No, you may not." Father Conrad instructed Brother Bernard, the kitchen master, "Lock up everything tonight."

Then Abbot Anthony told Father Conrad, "After what happened last night, you'd better stop bringing Sam to recreation. Of all things—monks brawling! It's shameful!"

"I didn't mean to hit him so hard," Father Conrad said. He was referring to Brother Rupert, the groundskeeper who had despised the dog from the very beginning, when he'd caught Sam lifting his leg to one of the newly-planted bushes bordering the church.

Father Conrad had tried removing the sign he knew Rupert had posted in the community room: NO DOGS ALLOWED. "Leave it alone," the groundskeeper yelled as he grabbed the novice master's arm. With his free arm, Father Conrad slugged Brother Rupert in the face.

Pressing a handkerchief to his bleeding nose, Brother Rupert shouted, "Get that damn animal out of here!"

"That mutt has no right being anywhere in the monastery," Father Gabriel yelled. He was the treasurer and complained about the cost of dog food and the trips to the veterinarian for rabies and distemper shots and heartworm testing. Sam fled from the community room with his tail between his legs.

Father Conrad followed behind him, but not before informing Father Gabriel, "Sam isn't a mutt. He's a purebred collie, registered with the American Kennel Club. I've got papers to prove it."

*   *   *

Later in the day, Novice Jeremiah revealed to Father Conrad that he was leaving the monastery. "I felt called to monastic life, but here I have found nothing that resembles it."

"I think you've made a good decision," Father Conrad said. "More than likely when the time came, the chapter members wouldn't have been in favor of your professing vows."

Just this morning, Father Nathaniel had told him, "That jerk isn't getting my vote."

"I've told my classmate that he'll have to finish the novitiate by himself. He's confident of receiving a favorable vote in this poor excuse of a monastery. This athletic club! You already have a swimming pool and tennis court, and you're talking about a golf course."

"We have these facilities because we run a boarding school for boys."

"It seems to me the monks use them much too often."

"Monks need physical exercise. You should have taken up swimming."

"I am not a jock, Father, like the young man who parades around the novitiate in athletic shorts and a tank top."

Father Conrad remembered sending them to work in the garden soon after the start of their novitiate, and telling Jeremiah, "You needn't wear your habit while picking beans."

"I refuse to shed my monastic identity," the newly-invested novice replied.

"Good grief," the novice master said under his breath. "One novice won't take off his habit and the other novice won't remove his earring."

*　　*　　*

"What was Novice Jack's response to your leaving?"

"He wanted to know if some woman eagerly awaited my return. I mentioned Judy, who works at the bank. I told him she was fond of me. He said, 'Hey, man, I bet your boobs are bigger than hers.'"

Father Conrad said, "You and he have not been the least bit compatible."

"I expect no charity from anyone in this monastery." There were tears in Jeremiah's eyes. "No one likes me. They are divided over the dog, but unanimous in their loathing of me."

For a moment, Father Conrad was tempted to speak words of consolation. Instead, he asked, "Would you like me to drive you to the bus depot in town?"

"I'll thumb a ride there."

"The walk to the highway will be good exercise," Father Conrad told him.

"I'll shake this place's dust from my feet. You were not worthy of my calling to a monastery that is beyond reform."

"Was that your purpose in coming here? You expected to reform us? Jeremiah, please do not attempt to enter another monastery," the novice master advised. "No monastic community wants a novice who thinks his vocation is to reform it."

That afternoon Father Conrad phoned the farmer who had recently purchased Angela Dunlop's property. Although he already had three dogs, the novice master coaxed him into taking the collie. "I'll bring Sam over right now," Father Conrad told the farmer.

As the monks entered the refectory for supper, Father Nathaniel slapped Father Conrad on the back, and said, "You did it. You got rid of them both. Congratulations!"

Kevin Zepper

Visitation

I was only five or six when my Grandpa Julius died. Most of my memories of him are faded, like sepia photos in a scrapbook. In one photo he's playing rummy with my father and the guys in my family. There was always room after Thanksgiving for rummy. I remember him, my grandpa, calling my father "Melly." "Good place for cards," Grandpa would say. Their rummy room later became my bedroom. Julius looked stone serious in every photo, even his wedding picture. When he did smile, it was well played. His features looking like granite turned flesh. I think he could have been a minister able to deliver any message with steady reverence. I didn't attend his funeral. I was too young to go. His rummy chair sat vacant and the rummy games left with him. I clearly remember Grandpa Julius. Shortly after his funeral, I grew terribly sick, in bed with a 104-degree temperature. I feared the growing inky corners of my room would somehow swallow me if I went to sleep. After nodding a few times I saw him in my bedroom next to the bed. He was wearing a black and red checked flannel shirt and dark brown pants. His face looked stern at first, then warmed into one of his rare smiles. He whispered to me as the darkness crept back into the corners of the bedroom, "It's okay, it's okay."

Contributor Notes

Maxine Adams

is a writer, poet, and photographer. She helped start the
Cabin Fever Writers Festival in Fergus Falls, Minnesota.
Born in Montana and a Minnesota resident since 1982,
Maxine currently serves as Executive Director for the Lake
Region Arts Council.

Luke Anderson

began writing creative nonfiction and poetry after retiring
from a career managing nonprofit organizations. Luke lives
in Battle Lake, Minnesota, and is a member of the Fergus
Falls Writers' Group and a founding member of the Lake
Region Writers Network, currently serving as its president.

Joe Baker

says watching an older brother encouraged him to dare
Conrad and Dostoyevsky. A junior high school teacher led
him near Hawthorne and Irving. Joe's father told brilliant
tales of the lakes region, and his children could not be more
proud that a street in Deer Creek bears the family name.

Frances Ann Crowley

is a graduate of Minnesota State University Moorhead with
a B.S. degree in education. She taught at Lake Park-Audubon
Schools for 27 years and is now employed part-time by
Detroit Lakes Public Schools as an adult basic education
instructor. Frances has had poems published in *Talking Stick*,
Lake Country Journal, and *Minnesota Moments*.

Holly Dowds

was raised in Minnesota. She received her B.A. cum laude
from Smith College and her Master's of Architecture from

the University of Minnesota. Raising two sons, Holly practiced architecture and taught before experiencing a brain injury. She currently lives in Minneapolis and is a participant at The Loft Literary Center.

Cindy Fox

dipped her toes into the writing waters in 2008. Reflections of her country life have appeared in *Farm & Ranch Living*, *Northwoods Woman*, and other publications. In 2012, Cindy was the creative nonfiction winner in *Talking Stick*. She credits Jackpine Writers' Bloc for encouraging her to dive into the water.

Yahya Frederickson

is a former Peace Corps volunteer in Yemen and Fulbright Scholar in Syria and Saudi Arabia, and is a professor at Minnesota State University Moorhead. He has authored three chapbooks; the most recent is *Month of Honey, Month of Missiles*. Yahya's poems have appeared recently in *Arts & Letters*, *Hanging Loose*, *Ninth Letter*, *The Southern Review*, and *Witness*.

Susan Gilbert

is originally from the UK. She has spent the last 20 years in Minnesota evolving from a computer systems programer/analyst into an artist. Susan works in a variety of media including: cast metal, human hair, tea stains and words. Susan's work explores the elusive moments that encapsulate a life.

Ruby Grove

is a retired English teacher and librarian. Writing and reading stories have been a big part of her life. Several of her stories, memoirs, and poetry have appeared in regional publications.

Theater, both acting and directing, is an additional passion. Ruby lives in Grand Forks, North Dakota.

Vinnie Hansen

was born and raised in South Dakota. She is the author of the *Carol Sabala Mystery Series*. Vinnie has written many published short stories and was a finalist for the Iowa School of Letters Award for Short Fiction. Retired from her career as an English teacher, Vinnie lives in Santa Cruz, California.

Audrey Kletscher Helbling

writes from Faribault, but with her poetry rooted deep in her native southwestern Minnesota prairie. She's been published in numerous anthologies, in the *Minneapolis Star Tribune*, on *Roadside Poetry* billboards and elsewhere, including in a poet-artist collaboration. Audrey also showcases her writing and photography via her *Minnesota Prairie Roots* blog.

Nancy Klepetka

is formally trained as a chiropractor and has spent the past 16 years treating clients in Alexandria, Minnesota. When she's not moving bones, she is gardening, biking or floating down a river with her family. Most recently, Nancy is delighted to be dancing with words.

Karla Klinger

is a retired UMM academic administrator, high school English teacher, and avocational potter. Karla's early poems appeared in St. Olaf student literary publications and in a national college collection. She hopes publication in the *Lake Region Review* will lead to a broader sharing of her poetry.

Elisa Korentayer

is a writer and singer/songwriter who performs as Elisa Korenne (www.elisakorenne.com). She performs shows about historical oddballs and has just finished her fifth album. Elisa is presently working on her first memoir, *Hundred Miles to Nowhere*, about moving from New York City to rural New York Mills, Minnesota.

Judy R. Korn

is a member of the Pomme de Terre Women Poets group in Morris, Minnesota.

Ryan Kutter

lives near Grey Eagle, Minnesota. He works in gardens, enjoys woodworking, and is studio manager at the Saint John's Pottery in Collegeville, Minnesota. Ryan is a student of poetry and many gifted teachers.

Julie C. Larson

has worked in higher education for 20 years and in secondary education for eight years before retiring in 2008. She lives in New Brighton, Minnesota, with her partner and their cat. Julie has been published in *Talking Stick* and the *Minnesota Daily*. She is currently working on a memoir.

Kim Larson

retired from mortgage lending in 2009 to pursue her dream of writing. She's taken creative writing classes at Concordia College and started a writing group. In 2011 her first non-fiction story was published in the *Lake Region Review 1*. She has two sons in college and lives in Moorhead, Minnesota, with her loving husband, Chuck.

Linda Frances Lein

has published four books: *Mother to Mother: Letters about Being a Mom* (1999), *Country Reflections* (2000), *Hannah Kempfer: An Immigrant Girl* (2002), and *The Making of a Small Town: Carlisle,*

Minnesota (2008). Linda is primarily a creative nonfiction writer, but she has published a few poems in *The Rambler*, *Red Weather* and now *Lake Region Review*. She also writes a blog about the craft of writing: http://www.LindaFrancesLein.WordPress.com.

Kathleen Lindstrom

has had short stories published in 22 magazines, e-zines and literary anthologies. She won the Arthur Edelstein Prize for Short Fiction. Kathleen's poem "Shrapnel" won first place in a 2007 poetry competition. She was a semi-finalist or earned honorable mentions in five other competitions.

Ethan Marxhausen

is a freelance writer and bookseller from Minneapolis, Minnesota. He recently graduated with a B.A. in English from Gustavus Adolphus College and is currently working on his first novel. Ethan thinks that fiction is the only thing you can take seriously anymore. He thinks that lemon zest goes with everything except peanut butter.

Linda Back McKay

is a Minneapolis poet, writer and teaching artist. Her latest poetry collections include: *The Next Best Thing* (2011 Nodin Press) and *The Cockeyed Precision of Time* (2007 White Space Press). Her newest nonfiction book is *Out of the Shadows: Stories of Adoption and Reunion* (2012 North Star Press). Website: www.lindabackmckay.com.

Travis Moore

was conceived a car length away from Minnesota. He likes to live vicariously through the dancers in the rain while pondering names of future children by the fire. But he remembers that to do things, to maintain, to lend an identity to 18 years of moral testing requires a lot of bent beans—complacent steps from the farmyard he mastered the truth in the lean. Travis realized before he got to the B's like Bianca and Bill that his hands aged without him—rain to snow. His recent publications include *Amalgam Blast*, *Red Weather*, and two poems in *Lake Region Review, Number 1*.

Kristine Price

is a writer and poet from St. Paul living in Monticello, Minnesota. She obtained her B.A. in creative writing from Metropolitan State University. Kristine is a two-time Loft Mentorship Series finalist and former features contributor for *The Wright County Journal Press*. In addition, her work has appeared in *Saint Paul Almanac* and *Haute Dish*.

Candace Simar

is a writer and poet from Pequot Lakes, Minnesota. A life-long Minnesotan, Candace nurtures a passion for Minnesota history and her Scandinavian heritage. She published four books in The Abercrombie Trail Series, of which *Birdie* received the 2012 Spur Award from the Western Writers of America. Her prose and poetry have received awards from the Bob Dylan Creative Writing Contest, the League of Minnesota Poets, the National Federation of State Poetry Societies, the *Lake Region Review* and Brainerd Writer's Alliance. Candace is a grateful recipient of Five Wings Art Grants funded in part by the McKnight Foundation. Website: www.candacesimar.com.

Doris Lueth Stengel

was born on the prairies of North Dakota, and transplanted to the woods and lakes of Minnesota by marriage. Doris writes about both. She likes best to write about "human nature" which often is tied to the landscape of one's life.

Doris is a member of Heartland Poets, League of Minnesota Poets and National Federation of State Poetry Societies. Her chapbook *Small Town Lines* was recently published by Finishing Line Press.

Liz Sweder

began writing a memoir three years ago when she joined the Fergus Falls Writing Group. After raising her family, she earned a B.F.A. in Sculpture and Ceramics from the University of Minnesota, Minneapolis. Liz grew up in Fergus Falls and Minneapolis, and now lives on Jewett Lake near Fergus Falls.

Francine Marie Tolf

is the author of *Rain, Lilies, Luck*, her first full-length collection of poetry, and *Joliet Girl*, a memoir, both published by North Star Press, St. Cloud, Minnesota. Francine's work has appeared in numerous journals. *Prodigal*, her second full-length poetry collection, was published by Pinyon Publishing in 2012.

Benet Tvedten

had been a Benedictine monk at Blue Cloud Abbey in South Dakota for 54 years. The monastery closed this summer and he is now at Assumption Abbey in North Dakota. Benet is the author of four books about monasticism and has had fiction published in various literary magazines.

Kevin Zepper

is an Instructor at Minnesota State University Moorhead. His fourth chapbook, *Sugartown*, was published by Finishing Line Press and is available through Amazon.com. When he's not writing, he's grading papers.

Get involved with the Lake Region Writers Network!

Whether you're a beginning or seasoned writer, whether you're a reader of creative writing, or a teacher, librarian, or bookstore owner ... the Lake Region Writers Network is for you.

There is no membership, no annual dues, no fine print, no swag or folderol ... just a lively community devoted to the literary arts.

Join us at our annual writers conference, a one-day event featuring noted writers, inspiring workshops, and the chance to eat good food in the company of interesting folks.

Visit our website at www.lakeregionwriters.net. You'll find:

- interesting essays on the craft and process of writing
- links to resources for writers
- a list of regional writers groups
- news about upcoming literary events in the region
- news about the annual writers conference and the *Lake Region Review*
- and more!

Join our mailing list and receive occasional emails of interest to writers and readers in the region.

And please find us on Facebook!

Call for New Work

Lake Region Review, Number 3 will appear in early autumn at the fifth annual Lake Region Writers Network 2013 Conference.

We seek quality fiction, creative nonfiction, and poetry by writers in Minnesota and the eastern Dakotas, especially from those with a personal connection to this region. The work submitted does not need to be grounded in the region, though we admit to a fondness for this region and a desire to see it represented in creative and engaging ways.

For writers guidelines, deadlines and other information, please visit our website at **www.lakeregionwriters.net**.

Writers interested in feedback are urged to seek a writers group. See our website for information about a writing group near you. Consult our website, too, for lively essays about the writing process and for other resources available to writers in this region.

We look forward to reading your work!

Charles Beck

About the Cover Artist

"Cardinals"

The cover art for Lake Region Review, Number 2 is a woodcut print design created by Charles Beck, one of the most recognized artists in Minnesota.

His woodcut prints are influenced by the landscape of Otter Tail County and the Scandinavian culture and values of his heritage. Beck's work is widely exhibited in local and regional art galleries, private collections, and in several publications of his work.

Charles Beck is a native of Fergus Falls, Minnesota, where he continues to live and work at the age of ninety. Beck studied art at Concordia College in Moorhead and earned his Master's in Fine Arts from the State University of Iowa. He was selected for inclusion in a show called *American Painting Today* at the Metropolitan Museum of Art in New York in 1950.

Beck continued art studies at the University of Minnesota, where he began working with woodcut prints. He taught at M State, Fergus Falls, for twenty-seven years and continues to be a major art influence and contributor in the region.